THE
WINDMILLS AND WATERMILLS OF WIRRAL

A HISTORICAL SURVEY

ROWAN PATEL

COUNTYVISE LTD

First Published 2016 by Countyvise Ltd
14 Appin Road, Birkenhead, CH41 9HH

Copyright © 2016 Rowan Patel

British Library Cataloguing in Publication Data.
A catalogue record for this book is available from the British Library.

ISBN 978 1 910352 10 6

Printed in Great Britain by Short Run Press Ltd., Exeter, Devon, EX2 7LW

ACKNOWLEDGEMENTS

This book represents the culmination of over eight years spent researching Wirral's mills, for my efforts to write the history of this subject began around November 2007. Work has been ongoing ever since and over the years I have received generous help from many individuals and organisations. The finished work could not have been so extensive if I had not benefited from the knowledge of others. Therefore, I would like to take the opportunity to thank the staff of Bebington, Birkenhead and Chester Reference Libraries, Cheshire Record Office and Wirral Archives. For the information which they generously provided, and in some cases for also providing photographs, I am very much indebted to Susan Nicholson of the Bromborough Society; Peter France and John Emmett of Wirral Archaeology; Professor Graham Connah of the Australian National University; the late Jim O'Neil; Mike Curtis; Dr. Paul Booth of the University of Keele; Simon Lightbound; Malcolm and Renie Verity of Merseyside Industrial Heritage Society; David Allan of the Eastham Archive Group and Ted Edwards.

For kindly providing me with photographs and paintings from their collections I also wish to express my sincerest gratitude to Dr. Ron Cookson of the Mills Archive Trust; Roger Lane and Dennis Clegg of the Heswall Society; Ian Boumphrey; Jane Gallagher of Special Collections at the Templeman Library, University of Kent; Colin Simpson of the Williamson Art Gallery and Museum; Greg Dawson; Ian Hughes and Birkenhead Reference Library. Cheshire Archives and Local Studies have generously allowed me to use extracts from tithe maps, estate maps and wills held at Cheshire Record Office; whilst Old-Maps and Ordnance Survey have kindly permitted me to use extracts of old Ordnance Survey maps, to which they reserve all rights.

I am very grateful to Dr. Barry Job of Etruria Industrial Museum, Stoke-on-Trent, who kindly offered to proofread my final manuscript, and provided many helpful suggestions. I would also like to thank my parents, Rachel, and Charles for all of their help, both in proofreading, and for much other assistance. I have been helped immensely by their continued support of this project, over many years. This book was originally to be printed by Countyvise Limited of Birkenhead. The text was handed over to them in February 2015 and they produced an initial proof, before their unfortunate closure several months later. I am deeply indebted to Cathy Roberts of Literally A Bookshop in New Brighton, for it was her valued help which allowed me to obtain Countyvise's electronic proof of the book. The layout is largely due to Countyvise, but I have edited the book to completion myself. My final thanks go to printers Short Run Press Limited of Exeter. They were responsible for printing the book, and readily offered their help and advice during the printing process. Lastly, I would be delighted to hear from anyone who has any queries, corrections or comments concerning this book - please do not hesitate to get in touch.

Rowan Patel,

Bromborough, December 2015

rowangp@yahoo.co.uk

CONTENTS

LIST OF ILLUSTRATIONS

PART 1: INTRODUCTION

CHAPTER 1: MILLING ON WIRRAL

The Wirral Peninsula is a place which has long had an association with milling. There have been watermills here for a millennium, whilst windmills have been a feature of the landscape for many centuries. The peninsula undoubtedly contained the highest concentration of windmills in Cheshire, for a remarkable number could once be found within this small area. Watermills were once generally a familiar feature within the county of Cheshire, yet they were not so common in Wirral's recent past, when windmills were the more common structure. All the same, there are ancient watermill sites on the peninsula which can boast great age. Any mill listed in the Domesday survey of 1086 is by definition a watermill, for windmills had yet to appear in this country. Whether the survey represents an entirely comprehensive record of Cheshire's mills at that time is open to debate, yet of the eighteen mills listed in Domesday Cheshire two of the sites are on Wirral, so there were doubtless watermills here before the Norman Conquest. Anglo-Saxon charters generally make only rare mentions of mills, yet the Domesday survey proves that watermills were a common feature of late Anglo-Saxon England.

Windmills were a later feature of the English landscape, appearing in the 1180s, centuries after the first watermills. Windmills are known to have been constructed on Wirral under a century after they first appeared. Early references here are at Poulton Lancelyn in 1279 and Storeton in 1284. These sites may well be the first recorded in the whole county of Cheshire. By 1291 windmills were widespread and the ecclesiastical taxation of Pope Nicholas IV conducted in that year shows windmills associated with many monastic establishments, including sites on Wirral. Monastic houses which held mills on Wirral were Birkenhead Priory, St. Werburgh's Abbey and Basingwerk Abbey. At the time of the dissolution, monastically held mills were confiscated and became the property of the Crown. Some former monastic estates and their mills were held by the Crown for some decades, but eventually the mills were generally sold into private ownership.

Two sandstone ridges run down the length of the peninsula, one on the Dee side and the other on the Mersey side. These ridges frequently break through a plain of clay, thus forming the sandstone outcrops visible at many points in the region. It was on these ridges that many of Wirral's villages were built and also where many windmills came to be constructed. The prevailing winds blowing onto the west coast of the country were ideal for powering windmills. Indeed, they continued to power some until relatively recent times. When I initially became interested in Wirral's mills I was disappointed to discover that there was no recent account describing them and their histories. The last major work which focused on the peninsula's windmills and watermills as a whole was Edward Mitford Abraham's 'The Old Flour Mills of Wirral', which was read to the Historic Society of Lancashire and Cheshire in 1903 and published in their *Transactions* of that year. Whilst a very useful reference the descriptions of remains were hardly reliable today. In all cases a reinvestigation has been undertaken to discover what has become of Wirral's once plentiful mills.

There is an attempt to record every mill site on the peninsula, along with the rest of Cheshire in Oliver Bott's 'Cornmill Sites in Cheshire 1066-1850'. This great undertaking was published in *Cheshire History* in six parts between 1982 and 1986 and for the most part forms a very comprehensive source. Some further information on Wirral's watermills has been provided by J. Harold Norris's survey of 'The Water-Powered Corn Mills of Cheshire'; this featured in the *Transactions of the Lancashire and Cheshire Antiquarian Society* in 1969. Dodgson's monumental survey of *The Place-Names of Cheshire* for the English Place-Name Society has also been consulted; Part 4 of this series covers the Wirral Hundred and details some obscure references to ancient mills.

The most recent general work on Wirral's windmills was a short paper entitled 'The Windmills of Wirral' by Hazel Williams and John Crompton. This appeared in the *Journal of the North-Western Society for Industrial Archaeology and History* in 1976 and furnished some useful information. I decided that I would record the history and examine the remains of Wirral's mills in the early 21st century, over a century after Mitford Abraham completed his account. The sources just mentioned are relied upon many times throughout and are referred to as "Mitford Abraham", "Norris", "Bott", "Dodgson" and "Williams and Crompton".

I have made careful examination of three early surveys of Cheshire. The first is Peter Burdett's *A Survey of the County Palatine of Chester* published in 1777. This is followed by Christopher Greenwood's *Map of the County Palatine of Chester from an Actual Survey made in the year 1819*. Finally, I have consulted Andrew Bryant's *Map of the County Palatine of Chester from an Actual Survey by A. Bryant in the years 1829, 1830 & 1831*; this was published in 1831. These three maps are my earliest general cartographic references and will be referred to throughout as "Burdett", "Greenwood" and "Bryant". There are also a number of surveys of the River Dee and Irish Sea, which mark windmills and predate Burdett's county survey. Sea charts referred to were surveyed by Collins (1689), Mackay-Math (1732), Fearon and Eyes (1738), Williamson (1766) and Burdett (1771), where bracketed dates are the years of publication. Earlier references to specific areas come from estate maps and field names where these are available. Later references were based on Ordnance Survey maps, starting with the first editions of 1840. Tithe maps of Cheshire have proved an extremely fruitful point of reference and field name evidence has also been extracted from these surveys.

Tithe maps were prepared for townships across the country as a result of the Tithe Commutation Act of 1836. In Cheshire, land was divided into numbered plots with the accompanying tithe apportionments providing information on who owned and occupied all of the land within a township, along with the names given to fields. Field names are referred to regularly later in this book. Fields were named centuries ago by those who worked the land and the names used were mainly communicated orally. These names were recorded on estate maps and tithe maps. Field names were generally written down only infrequently and this sometimes led to considerable corruption of the written names between different sources. The tithe apportionments provide the largest scale record of field names; some names were of ancient foundation whilst others were more modern. They provide an important record, for fields were usually named logically based on local features such as mills, which may have long since disappeared.

Burdett's map published in 1777 is acknowledged to be the most accurate early survey of the county of Cheshire which clearly marks such features as windmills and watermills. This is the earliest detailed survey I have consulted and every mill on the map has a section of its own in Part 2 of the book. I believe that Part 2 includes a section on every mill to have existed in the area from the 1770s onwards. It has been suggested that certain aspects of Burdett's survey work were somewhat hurriedly executed. However, the survey still stands out as a significant accomplishment in late 18th century cartography and it was many decades before it was surpassed in Cheshire. It is sometimes assumed that the surveying of Burdett's map dated to around the time of publication. However, it should be noted that the survey was actually conducted between 1772 and 1774. Burdett was a resident of Liverpool whilst carrying out his survey, but left the country to escape debt in 1774, at which point it is assumed his fieldwork had already been completed.

There were of course also some ancient mills which had disappeared before Burdett's 18th century survey, in some cases many centuries before. I have tried to cover these mills too and have described as many as I have found true evidence for in Part 3 of the book. There are many further mill sites in addition to those covered in Part 2 and only those which can be supported by a primary reference have been selected for Part 3. Whilst the sites listed in Part 2 were all covered by Mitford Abraham many in Part 3 were not. He does not appear to have examined older references covering medieval mills, for his 1903 account was primarily focussed on those mills which had ceased working in the relatively recent past.

Much of the evidence for these older mills comes from transcriptions and analyses of ancient documents, which were published in the *Cheshire Sheaf*; a column in the *Chester Courant* and later the *Cheshire Observer* where research was published by local historians. The column was bound annually between 1878 and 1978 in numerous series and with a number of editors. The most long-standing editor of the *Cheshire Sheaf* was William Fergusson Irvine, who helped organise the publication for nearly sixty five years. His contribution to Wirral's local history was vast and he is referred to as Irvine throughout this book. For some forty two years he edited the publication jointly with fellow Cheshire historian J. H. E. Bennett. Other eminent Wirral historians of this era, the works of whom have been consulted, include Ronald Stewart-Brown, John Brownbill and Frank Beazley. Some of the ancient documents drawn upon are in the form of inquisitions post mortem. These are medieval enquiries recording the deaths of tenants-in-chief who held land directly from the Crown, intended to ascertain whether any income was due to the Crown. If a mill was a component of the deceased's estate this could be mentioned, hence these are a very useful source. Further inquisitions post mortem, to those in the *Cheshire Sheaf*, were reproduced in George Ormerod's groundbreaking *History* of Cheshire published in 1819. Volume 2 of this work covers the Wirral Hundred and furnished some useful references to support little known sites. Mention must also be made of the *Transactions of the Historic Society of Lancashire and Cheshire*, in which very well researched and learned papers have been published since 1849. A vast quantity of information may be gathered from these extensive volumes. Useful and obscure details have also been gleaned from the original documents published by The Record Society of Lancashire and Cheshire and by the Chetham Society.

There are also further sites where I have found no documentary evidence to substantiate a mill's existence. However, based on field name evidence the presence of mills at some of these sites is extremely likely, even if it is not confirmed by primary documentation. Field names can preserve the memory of ancient sites where no evidence, written or physical, is known. Mill related field names suggest proximity to a mill site, since this is the main rationale for them being named as such. The tithe maps of Cheshire record field names in detail for all townships and in some instances earlier estate maps from local landowners may denote previous incarnations of those field names. Part 5 of Bott's survey is titled 'Evidence from Field Names', and provides his interpretation of relevant tithe apportionments. I too have made a thorough examination of field name evidence to present further sites. There are also locations where primary references to mills are known, but the probable sites where these mills stood could not be deduced, meaning they could not justify individual sections in Part 3. Additionally, examples are known where a historian may have stated that a mill existed in their secondary account, but I have found no primary evidence. All of these sites are listed within Chapter 9 in Part 4. Some are very likely sites, others seem less probable, but are included for completeness as they are not easily written off entirely. Given the dearth of any true evidence there is little to say about some of these sites, which are by their very nature hard to date and interpret.

In this book I shall focus on the area of land which originally constituted the historic Hundred of Wirral, an ancient administrate area and one of the Cheshire Hundreds. The administrative area designated as a "Hundred" was initially one which contained one hundred hides. The hide was an Anglo-Saxon unit, initially based upon an area of land capable of supporting a single family. The hide varied in area based on the land's value; later a hide was related to an area eligible for a certain land tax. Cheshire was split into Hundreds in the Domesday Book of 1086. At some point before 1200 the Cheshire Hundreds were reorganised and land originally within the boundaries of Wirral, was placed within neighbouring Broxton Hundred. The area of the 13th century Wirral Hundred existed unchanged, until Hundreds became obsolete as a result of a Local Government Act of 1894. This Wirral Hundred is the area whose mills will be considered within this book.

Three of the original boundaries of the Wirral Hundred were of course, the estuaries of the Rivers Mersey and Dee and the Irish Sea. The southern boundary of the Hundred was formed by the Broxton Valley. This valley is a glacial feature, running from a point before the River Gowy flows into the River Mersey at Stanlow Point, up to the River Dee at Blacon Point. Its course is now approximated by the Shropshire Union Canal. The southern boundary of Wirral, from Blacon Point up to the Dee estuary at Burton Point, is represented by the old shoreline of the River Dee. Since the local government reforms of 1974, the peninsula has been split in two and administered by several different local authorities. However, no attention will be paid to these modern day, political boundaries. Historically speaking, the entire peninsula remains an important part of the old County of Chester.

In many instances the locations where Wirral's mills stood were ancient. The mill buildings were often continuously renewed so as to account for any advances in technology. Occasionally an entire rebuilding would occur and in this way some mills lasted for many centuries. With the coming of steam, windmills and watermills found it hard to compete. The industrial revolution saw the development of steam mills containing many pairs of millstones. Later on, during the 1870s, grinding on a large scale using metal rollers was developed; these roller mills spelt the end of traditional milling using grindstones. Wind and water power could compete no longer. The old, small scale technology was no match for the large steam roller mills, such as those constructed at Birkenhead, Wallasey and Ellesmere Port Docks. Milling using wind and water power gradually became less economical. Some traditional mills were modernised by fitting steam engines to drive their mechanisms. Several of Wirral's mills struggled on in this manner during the last years of their lives, before finally being closed altogether. There is slight regional variation in the date at which traditional flour mills ceased to be used. It seems that the roller mills built on Wirral's docklands, and in Liverpool, spelt an earlier demise for wind and water power here, than in some other more remote areas.

Mills have fallen out of use from the earliest times and Wirral holds the sites of some ancient mills, which disappeared centuries ago. However, there are also some ancient sites which worked continuously, right into the 20th century. By the 19th century the core body of remaining local mills on Wirral had been unchanged for some time. Some mills disappeared during the early 19th century, but progressing through that century the closures became more frequent as the second industrial revolution gathered pace. Industrialisation led to the depopulation of the countryside across the country. As towns like Birkenhead expanded, the nature of Wirral's workforce changed; more people being employed in urbanised districts, with less land being under cultivation and less need for local grain mills. The rapid industrialisation and urbanisation of parts of Wirral meant the area was no longer based around a primarily rural economy. The construction of steam mills at local ports also had a detrimental effect and by the 1870s Wirral's remaining mills were closing with alarming regularity. It was a gradual change; the mills fell out of use over the course of some decades. Between 1870 and 1910 the majority of Wirral's remaining mills had ceased working.

Of the mills that survived, most stopped milling grain and turned to the production of animal feed, for this was not so competitive. Addressing a less competitive market allowed some mills to continue working into the 20th century. All the same, by the start of that century most of Wirral's mills had already closed. For an area once so rich in mills, just two windmills and a watermill survived in use after 1920. Of these mills only the windmills continued to work via their traditional power source. The remaining mills were Willaston mill (closed 1930, partially wind, partially engine powered), the Gibbet mill (closed 1926, wind powered) and Bromborough watermill (closed 1940, powered by an engine since 1910). These three mills were the last working remnants of Wirral's milling past. After they had closed the traditional means of producing flour by wind and water were entirely obsolete on the Wirral Peninsula. Milling with grindstones was no longer a commercially sustainable enterprise, but was forever consigned to the history of this area. This book attempts to record that history for it is a neglected area of Wirral's past, never covered in detail within a single piece of work.

CHAPTER 2: A BRIEF HISTORY OF MILLING

2.1 The Milling Process

Grinding cereals by water and wind power was a logical progression, to mechanise a process which had been carried out since prehistory. People used tools of stone to process their cereals from the most primeval times. Adam Lucas writing in his definitive *Wind, Water, Work: Ancient and Medieval Milling Technology* mentions a grinding stone dated to 28,000 BC from New South Wales; this is 20,000 years older than examples from the Northern Hemisphere. Stone milling tools include a variety of crushing and grinding devices of which prehistoric examples exist in Britain. The history of these most archaic handmilling devices is covered by Richard Bennett and John Elton in Volume 1 of their monumental *History of Corn Milling*, published in four volumes between 1898 and 1901. Volume 2 of this work covers windmills and watermills and proved an important reference in the Introduction to this book.

The rotary quern, which was known before the birth of Christ and which remains in use in some parts of the world, crushes grain between two stones, the upper one of which rotates. The mills which this book covers harnessed the principal powers of nature to mechanise this same form of rotary grinding. As one of the oldest industries and one where the structures and principles remained little changed for many centuries, an examination of windmills and watermills provides a unique field of study. This area allows the industrial archaeologist to study a time period which generally extends well outside their remit.

The milling process involves making flour by grinding cereals such as wheat. Pairs of millstones were used for grinding and for many centuries a mill contained just a single pair of stones. Later on, with the rise of industry, larger mills were constructed which contained multiple pairs. The bottom millstone, known as the bed stone, was thicker than its partner and was affixed firmly to the floor of the mill. The top millstone was known as the running stone and this was free to turn on top of the bed stone. A minute gap was maintained between the two stones. Grooves called furrows were cut into the stones from a central hole to the edge of the millstone. The pattern of furrows used remained remarkably unchanged from Roman times. Grain contained in hoppers on the floor above the millstones was shaken into the eye; the hole in the centre of the millstone. As the running stone crushed the cereal against the bed stone it produced flour which flowed out of the furrows and was collected.

Early millstones in medieval times would probably have been quarried nearby. On Wirral these could have been formed from the harder types of local Cheshire sandstone.

An early 15th century reference to Irby mill records that millstones were obtained from Little Christleton. Another 15th century reference, this one to Burton mill, records that a millstone was brought from the gritstone edge at Congleton. There were several types of millstone which saw use in this country, in the post-medieval era of traditional milling. Traditionally, millstones of Derbyshire gritstone were used to crush barley and these were referred to as grey or peak stones. In later years the grey stones were commonly relegated to the production of animal feed. Cullin or blue stones were made from an igneous rock and imported from Germany. These were primarily used for grinding both barley and oats, but were not so common in Britain as on the continent. A harder stone, better suited for finer grinding, was the French burr stone, made from a type of quartz quarried near Paris. These were formed from sections which were joined using plaster of Paris and bound using iron bands. The French burr stones were used for grinding wheat into flour and were the most common type of millstone used in this country, alongside those from Derbyshire.

Wirral's ancient windmills and watermills would have originally been a component of a manorial society. As in other areas of the country, mills within the feudal system were generally under the laws of milling soke. These soke rights meant that the lord of the manor, or sometimes an ecclesiastical establishment, had the sole right to build a mill within their manor, construction of other mills being prohibited. The lord's tenants within the manor were compulsorily obliged to grind their grain at the manorial mill. This meant that the lord commanded a monopoly on flour production within their manor, a powerful position, which was open to exploitation. The construction of a mill for the use of residents of the manor can be seen as a philanthropic gesture. However, the soke rights which required tenants to grind at the feudal mill also provided a reliable source of income for the manorial lord.

2.2 Types of Windmill and Watermill

The Post Mill

According to Lucas the post mill originated in Western Europe, possibly in England, and was amongst the earliest designs of windmill used for grinding grain. It was possibly the first windmill to employ sails in a vertical position. An earlier design with horizontally orientated sails was of Persian origin and has been suggested to have provided the inspiration for the European post mill. Post mills were the first windmills to appear on the English landscape, yet they survived with only minor alterations, from when first introduced, up until the demise of the traditional windmill. Lucas felt there to be no conclusive evidence of windmills in England prior to 1180. Amongst the earliest references covered by Lucas is a windmill associated with Chichester Cathedral in 1180-1185. Another early mill dated

1185 was at Weedley, near the Humber in Yorkshire's East Riding. There are also some pre-13th century references to post mills over the English Channel, but none of these are reported to be any earlier than the first English windmills.

The post mill consisted of a wooden body containing all of the milling machinery and bearing the sails. This body was built centrally around a vertical wooden post, which was generally formed from a trunk of oak. The body of the mill was suspended from the crowntree, a horizontal beam attached to the top of the post, and could be rotated about the post in order to bring the sails into the prevailing wind. This action was achieved by hand using a wooden lever, the tailpole, which projected from the building. The miller would push the tailpole, thus rotating the entire structure, which turned with the crowntree. In later incarnations the tailpole sometimes had a wheel attached which rested on a paved track around the mill's circumference; this eased rotation. Post mills were simple structures and the early examples contained a single pair of millstones, although later structures often housed two pairs.

In their analysis of post mills Bennett and Elton split them into three main types. The earliest of these designs they termed the tripod post mill. The main post of any post mill is supported in a vertical position by means of an arrangement of wooden beams. Two horizontal beams which cross at ninety degrees and support the main post at their intersection are known as the crosstrees. Four diagonal cross-members connect the extreme ends of the crosstrees to the post and these are known as the quarterbars. The tripod post mill provided no protection for this wooden substructure, which was left exposed to the elements. Writing in *Harvesting the Air; Windmill Pioneers in Twelfth-Century England* Edward Kealey provided some discussion as to the origins and evolution of the post mill's substructure. He suggested that the main post was initially simply embedded in the ground, and supported by simple quarterbars which were also embedded. Archaeological evidence of this form has been discovered as mentioned by Smith in 'The English Medieval Windmill'. Crosstrees and further refinements came later as the necessity of additional support became clear.

Originally, the crosstree and quarterbar structure probably rested directly upon the ground. This led to a short lifetime since the wood was prone to becoming rotten. One improvement was to raise the structure off the ground on stone plinths; this form evolved from the most basic tripod mill, but was amongst the most long-lived. Another type of post mill was the sunk post mill. This variant existed alongside the basic tripod mill from very early in windmill history and was a popular means of construction. According to Bennett and Elton, examples of both tripod and sunk post mills were already known in Britain by the early 14th century. When building a sunk post mill a hole was excavated such that the mill's crosstrees could be buried beneath the ground. This provided additional stability over the basic tripod mill, which was especially susceptible to being blown down. It also provided a more sturdy foundation for a structure which often vibrated considerably whilst in use. However, the woodwork was especially vulnerable to the threat of rotting in the sunken form, and ultimately the tripod style raised upon stone plinths prevailed.

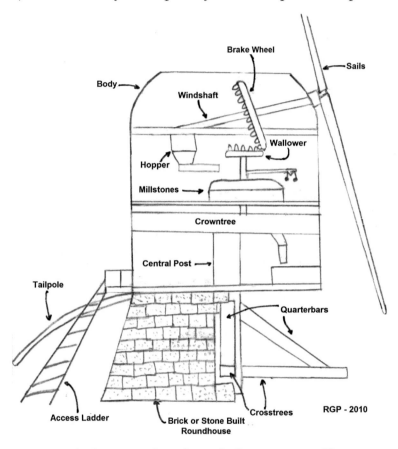

1. A cross-section of a typical turret post mill.

The most advanced post mill design involved raising the crosstrees and quaterbars above the ground and enclosing them in a roundhouse of brick or stone. This was built around the structure, thus protecting it from the weather and creating a considerably more substantial edifice known as a turret post mill. It is unclear when the roundhouse became a dominant feature and it may not have become common until the 18th century. Despite being a design of great antiquity, post mills continued to be built on Wirral into the 18th century. These later post mills were of the turret type and some survived until the very end of traditional milling on the peninsula. Other post mills on Wirral, even those which existed into the late 18th and early 19th centuries, are of unknown type. Some may have had roundhouses whilst others may have been of the more basic tripod type. Constructional details were seldom recorded and a lack of pictures adds to our ignorance. Knowledge is more lacking still for the little recorded post mills listed in Part 3; it is unknown what proportion of these mills were of the tripod type, sunk type or of any further unknown variants.

The Tower Mill

The tower mill was a later design of windmill which according to Lucas was known in the Mediterranean from the 15th century; although he suggests these mills did not begin to supplant the post mill in England until the 16th century. Langdon and Watts writing a paper on 'Tower Windmills in Medieval England' have suggested anomalous instances of tower mills in England as early as the late 13th century, and state that they were established technology by the 15th century. Either way, the construction of tower mills was attended with greater expense than that of post mills, which were never entirely ousted. Tower mills probably first appeared on Wirral in the 18th century. These mills consisted of a tower of brick or stone and on top of this tower a moveable cap was constructed, to which the sails were attached. Tower mills employed a mechanism whereby the sails could be turned into the wind by rotating the cap. The earliest tower mills had caps which were turned by hand using a lever equivalent to a post mill's tailpole, which extended down towards the ground. This method of achieving rotation was generally superseded fairly early on. In some places in England its use seems to have persisted into the 20th century. This was not the case on Wirral, where the only certain use of a tailpole on a tower mill was at Bidston in the early 19th century. A painting of unverified reliability also appears to show a tailpole in use at Thingwall. However, it seems likely that some of Wirral's other tower mills could have used tailpoles early on, especially any mills which were working in the 18th century.

Tower mills, or certainly those on Wirral, generally had a large pulley attached to the back of the cap, opposite the sails. An endless chain ran over this pulley and hung vertically down the exterior of the mill. Pulling the chain and turning the pulley would rotate the cap by means of gearing engaged with a rack which ran around the top wall of the tower. Reynolds, writing in *Windmills & Watermills*, suggested this means of turning the cap was devised in the early 18th century. Once the cap was in its intended position the chain could be affixed by means of cleats which protruded from the tower. Different styles of cap were used in different regions. Wirral tower mills generally had a boat shaped cap, the most common style in North West England. There were local variations of this boat shape in Cheshire, Lancashire and Anglesey, presumably introduced by local millwrights. The obvious advantage over a post mill was that the tower mill could be built much taller, due to its sturdier nature. It was no longer necessary to move the entire building into the wind.

Many later tower mills, especially those which were particularly tall, were built with a stage. The stage was an elevated walkway which ran around the circumference of the building, some way off the ground. This gave the miller access to the sails and the chain which turned the cap. If the mill did not have a stage then the miller accessed these parts of the mill from ground level. Wirral's earliest tower mills were built in the 18th century. The common local design in this period was a relatively short tower of three storeys with no stage; these mills generally contained two pairs of millstones. By the 19th century a taller tower of four or five storeys with a stage was the pattern favoured on Wirral. These could and did accommodate more than two pairs of millstones. Although one can find windmills with various numbers of sails in other parts of the country, all of Wirral's tower mills employed four sails.

In 1745 Edmund Lee took out the patent on the fantail, a means he had conceived by which the turning of a windmill's sails might be automated. This ingenious device was a small set of sails mounted on the back of the cap, in the same place as the chain driven pulley on less advanced mills. The fantail automated the turning of the cap, thus saving a lot of work for the miller. It was positioned perpendicular to the main sails, meaning that when the fantail was turned by the wind the main sails did not turn, but when the main sails turned the fantail did not. The device was connected to the gearing which rotated the cap.

If the main sails were not facing the wind then the fantail would be, so it would rotate and in doing so it would turn the cap along with the main sails. Eventually the main sails would be in the right position and they would start to turn. The fantail would no longer be facing the wind so it would not turn, hence the cap stopped turning and the main sails would remain in the right position to catch the wind. If the wind changed direction the fantail would turn and the process would begin again. The method worked so well that some old post mills were modernised by attaching a fantail to the tailpole, although this did not happen to any of Wirral's post mills. The fantail became a common 19th century feature in some parts of the country. However this was not the case on Wirral; most of Wirral's tower mills continued to use the old method where the cap was rotated by means of an endless chain right up until closure. Only one mill on Wirral is known to have had a fantail fitted, this being the Gibbet mill at Great Saughall.

There were also advances which occurred in terms of sails. Early mills used sails which were a simple wooden lattice. This framework would have a cloth called a sailcloth spread over it, thus maximising the surface area in contact with the wind. These sails were called common sails. Sailcloths needed to be changed every so often and also required re-positioning and tightening upon their wooden frames. Different amounts of the sail were covered in cloth depending on the conditions and different amounts of cloth could also be used to control the speed. The cloths needed to be adjusted accordingly depending on the strength of the wind. The main brake on the windshaft had to be engaged when the cloths were being adjusted and so apart from taking a lot of the miller's time, it also meant valuable time was lost when the mill could have been doing work.

An advance in terms of sails was the use of spring sails, devised by the millwright Andrew Meikle around 1772. These were composed of frames on which many wooden shutters were affixed, somewhat similar to a Venetian blind. The shutters were held closed by a spring and would open when the wind hit the sail, allowing the wind to pass through. The miller was able to alter the tension in the springs and this allowed them to control the speed at which the sails turned. There were further improvements on spring sails with provision for the angle of the shutters to be altered whilst the sails themselves were turning. The most popular modified form were known as patent sails; first used in 1807, these were conceived by the millwright William Cubitt. The invention of spring sails, and later patent sails, were major improvements to the traditional windmill, which greatly improved its efficiency. As with the fantail, only the Gibbet mill benefited from the development of spring sails. All of Wirral's other windmills retained common sails throughout their working lives.

On both windmills and watermills the main drive system of gears evolved their own individual names. In the tower mill the sails were connected to the windshaft, which rotated with the sails. This rotating shaft was connected to the brake wheel, which transmitted the power through ninety degrees to the wallower. The wallower was on the end of the main shaft, which turned vertically within the mill. On the other end of the shaft was the great spur wheel which was geared to the millstones via stone nuts. Larger mills would have multiple pairs of millstones positioned around the great spur wheel. The very early tower mills contained just one pair of stones, but all known examples on Wirral are believed to have contained at least two pairs. Various other pieces of machinery could be powered off the main shaft. The sack hoist for example was used for raising sacks of grain to a windmill's upper floors. The flour dresser was a mechanical sieve which could remove chaff and husks from the flour produced. In early post mills a single pair of millstones was driven directly from the brake wheel. Post mills with two pairs of millstones had another gear, the tail wheel, mounted on the windshaft and this drove the additional pair of millstones via a second wallower. A detailed study of the windmill and its machinery in Britain is included in Rex Wailes's classic text, *The English Windmill*, a book which is highly recommended.

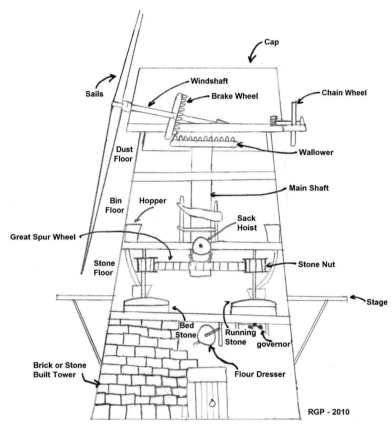

2. A cross-section of a typical tower mill.

The Watermill

Using the power of water to drive a waterwheel and power milling machinery is a practice of greater antiquity than milling by wind. The first evidence of watermills is, according to Lucas, of those which used a vertical waterwheel on a horizontal axle, with the power transferred through ninety degrees to the millstones. This system is the same as that which remained in commercial use into living memory and Lucas suggested that such mills first appeared "within the Graeco-Roman eastern Mediterranean some time between the beginning of the second and the end of the first centuries BCE, or possibly a little earlier". The Romans introduced mills of this type to Britain and mills built on this principle are often said to be of the Roman type. Archaeologically speaking, evidence of watermills is relatively scarce in Roman Britain. However, the technical competency of the Romans has long suggested that they may well have made wide use of water power in Britain.

A second type of watermill employed a wheel in the horizontal position, attached to a vertical axle. The mill building could be built directly over, or next to the stream and the wheel positioned in the current. The millstones could then be directly connected to the shaft of the waterwheel, no gearing being required. These mills are variously referred to as the Greek or Norse type of watermill. The Norse mill was a much simpler design than the Roman mill and has frequently been assumed to predate it. Bennett and Elton for example dated the Norse mill to before the Roman type, as did John Reynolds writing in his *Windmills & Watermills* of 1970. However, more recently Lucas has suggested that there is no evidence for this horizontal type of watermill before the 3rd century.

The Romans left Britain in the 5th century and according to Lucas it is not until the end of the 7th century that archaeological evidence of watermills has been found in the post-Roman period. Post-Roman Britain has yielded archaeological evidence of both Roman and Norse mills. It would appear that the simpler construction and easier operation of the Norse mill led to them finding favour in Anglo-Saxon England. They were later to be replaced by the Roman mill, but remained in use on some remote Scottish islands until the early 20th century. Hence, the Norse and Roman mill worked side by side one another for many centuries in Anglo-Saxon times. But where there is a lack of archaeological evidence, it is generally unclear which type of mill was in use at any given site. It is accepted that the watermills recorded in Domesday likely represented a mixture of both types, possibly with mills of lower value being of the Norse type. However, the vertical wheeled Roman mill is thought to have been predominant, and by the time of the Conquest Norse mills were losing popularity. Watts writing in *Water and Wind Power* has suggested that the Norse mill had effectively been entirely displaced in England two centuries after the Norman Conquest.

This means that although it is likely that Wirral's Domesday mills were of the Roman type, the possibility of them being Norse mills cannot be disregarded. No evidence is known of Norse mills existing on the peninsula, but in the case of early references one cannot be sure which kind of mill is referred to. Roman mills employing vertical waterwheels fell into several categories depending on the type of waterwheel used. The undershot waterwheel was turned by water forcing its way beneath the wheel. A series of paddles protruding at regular intervals from the rim of the wheel came into contact with the water and a flow of water underneath caused it to rotate. The overshot waterwheel had a series of compartments built around its circumference. Water was directed onto the wheel from above which caused the compartments to fill with water; this made the wheel unbalanced causing it to rotate and the water to spill out.

Raby mill had an overshot waterwheel, whilst Bromborough and Little Stanney mills both had undershot waterwheels. There were other waterwheel types such as the breastshot and pitchback wheels, but to my knowledge none of Wirral's mills employed these variations. Although there are numerous references to medieval watermills on Wirral, they were not nearly as common as windmills in more recent centuries. Some of the later watermills conformed to the pattern described by Norris in his 'The Water-Powered Corn Mills of Cheshire'; that is a three storey building with gearing on the ground floor, milling machinery on the first floor and storage space on the second floor.

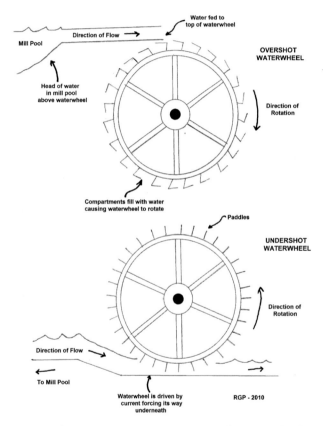

3. A comparison of the two major types of vertical waterwheel used on Wirral.

Undershot and overshot wheels are of similarly long foundation and both were described at a similar time, shortly before the birth of Christ. Simple horizontal wheels of Norse type could be positioned directly alongside a natural stream, or even in the stream itself. Generally a quantity of water might be diverted along a simple channel, which passed through the mill, and then flowed back into the stream itself. This was also a very practical setup with the vertical undershot waterwheel. However, the water in an unregulated stream would not provide a constant force. It often proved difficult to regulate the amount of water diverted, thus making it difficult to control the speed of rotation. Heavy rain could provide strong currents which might damage the waterwheel, whilst a lack of water might render the mill useless.

Such fluctuations in the rate of flow led to the damming of streams and consequential formation of mill pools. These pools provided large reserves of water, which the miller could exercise some control over. The mill pool would be connected to the waterwheel via an artificial channel called a leat. A sluice gate across the leat could be used to control the volume of water released. When researching ancient sites it is often uncertain what type of waterwheel was in use, especially if archaeological evidence is lacking. A site in a valley, where the available head of water lay above the location of the mill can suggest an overshot wheel. Flatter sites, where any mill pool was on a similar level to the mill itself, are more indicative of working by an undershot wheel.

On the coast and where there was a suitable tidal range, watermills were constructed which obtained their power from the tide. Such mills were built on coastal rivers with tidal influence, estuaries and harbours. These are called tide mills and several types were constructed which employed the tide in slightly different ways. They were known in England in Anglo-Saxon times and Lucas mentioned one in Kent which was referred to in a charter of 949. Tidal waters could be impounded either by linking the tidal zone to the mill pool via a channel, or by damming the area under tidal influence. Tidal waters would flow through a gateway and were retained once it was closed. The release of the tidal water could then be regulated and the watermill operated in the normal manner.

Another type of tide mill is said to have operated a waterwheel in a narrow channel. The flood tide would force its way past the waterwheel rotating it in one direction. A system of reverse gearing is said to have been employed such that the waterwheel could also be turned as the water receded on the ebb. However, Lucas has justifiably expressed some doubt as to how such gearing would have worked and does not allude to any mills working on this principle in England. He mentioned at least one tide mill with two waterwheels, operating separate sets of millstones at either side of the building; one waterwheel working on the incoming and one on the outgoing tide.

The Mersey estuary was the site of an 18th century tide mill on Wallasey Pool and other sites will be mentioned which could have operated on tidal principles. The ancient watermill at Bromborough, which may have been of Anglo-Saxon foundation, appears to have been worked as a tide mill. Certainly the mill within this township stood at a tidally influenced location from the 14th century. A second notable example is the Birkenhead Priory watermill, which existed in the 13th century. This is believed to have stood on Wallasey Pool, at a position which would have been significantly influenced by the tides, hence it may well provide a second example of an early tide mill on Wirral.

The names of the gears in a watermill were in some cases the same as those in a windmill. The waterwheel was attached to the main axle and on the other end of this was the pit wheel. The pit wheel transferred power through ninety degrees to the wallower, which in turn transferred it to the spur wheel. The spur wheel was once again coupled to stone nuts which were attached via shafts to the millstones. Other milling machinery was driven by belts, from a line shaft powered by the crown wheel. The systems are in fact fairly similar, except that in a windmill the power source is at the top and power is transferred down to the stones. In a watermill the power source is at the base of the mill with the stones on a higher level, hence the transfer of power proceeds upwards rather than downwards.

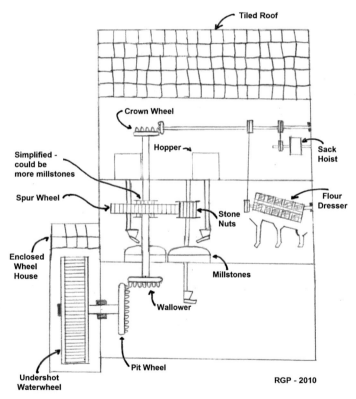

4. A cross-section of a typical watermill employing a vertical waterwheel.

2.3 Effects of Industrialisation

Waterwheels represented the primary source of power early in the industrial revolution, from around 1760 to the end of the 18th century. It was only in the 19th century that the steam engine reached a state of refinement such as to become the waterwheel's competitor. The principles of milling using wind and water had been understood for centuries before the industrial revolution. However, the technical developments which came with the revolution improved these ancient prime movers. Industrialisation revolutionised the ancient craft of milling and both windmills and watermills were subject to the biggest changes they had seen for centuries. The fundamentals of milling grain before and after the revolution remained unchanged; hence it makes sense to study Wirral's milling history, before and after industrialisation, as a whole.

Despite the logic of discussing mills from after the industrial revolution alongside those of earlier times, some of the features of 19th century mills were very far removed from the simplicity of previous centuries. The rise of industrialisation in Britain was marked with ambitious changes in mill design, with millwrights developing larger, more complex structures, based on the same motive power. These changes allowed wind and water powered grain mills to rise to their pinnacle of efficiency. However, the technological advances of the time were simultaneously improving the steam engine, alongside the old wind and water powered engines. Hence, the same technical breakthroughs which improved wind and water power ultimately reared the competitor which ensured their demise.

Some of the developments which were the result of industrialisation have already been mentioned. The tall tower mills of the 19th century were very much a product of industrialisation; windmills of a previously unseen magnitude became common during the industrial revolution. Refinements such as fantails and patent sails reflect the improvements to old technology which prevailed during the rise of British industry. Improvements to watermills were mainly based on changes in the design of the waterwheel. One of the key materials which defined the industrial revolution was iron, the price of which fell as the smelting process became more economically efficient. Ancient waterwheels would have been made entirely of wood. Later waterwheels were primarily of wood, but with iron fastenings, and this was the common form of construction until the mid-18th century.

Industrialisation led to the adoption of waterwheels made entirely or primarily of iron. The drive for more power in operations unassociated with grain milling, such as the mining and textile industries, led to the creation of larger waterwheels. Eventually the limitations of a primarily wooden structure became clear and cast iron started to be used, especially for the rims of large waterwheels where stresses were high. The first use of cast iron for milling machinery is generally credited to the civil engineer John Smeaton. He believed his use, in 1754, of cast iron for gears and shafts at the Carron Ironworks in Stirling, to be the first within a mill. Cast iron was heavily employed in waterwheel construction from the 1790s onwards, but spokes and paddles were generally still made of wood. Watts, writing in *Water and Wind Power*, has stated that waterwheels made entirely of iron were rare until the mid-19th century. Eventually iron was sufficiently cheap that even the modest local cornmill might have a waterwheel of all iron construction.

Cast iron was also to become a more prevalent feature in the mechanisms of later windmills. The windshaft which carried the sails was formed from wood for centuries, but was often cast in iron for windmills built during the industrial period. In both windmills and watermills gears were traditionally made of wood and were impressive feats of carpentry, requiring the complex assembly of many individual components. Oak was the most popular wood, followed by elm, beech and hornbeam. Very early gears were lantern pinions consisting of wooden staves held between two disks. Other early gears were of compass arm construction; a weak method of building gears where mortising weakened the structure. Later gears were of clasp arm construction, which Rex Wailes writing in *The English Windmill* in 1954, considered to be universal in those wooden geared mills which remained at that time.

Wooden gears needed to be renewed periodically, but could have a lifetime of some forty years. They continued in use until the end of the local grain mill; certainly on Wirral many mills employed wooden gearing until the end. However, in later mills cast iron was also used for gears, small gears like stone nuts being cast in one piece and larger ones in sections. There is evidence of cast iron gearing remaining at some mill sites on Wirral; the effects of the industrial revolution led to the use of iron even at very small local sites.

PART 2: MILLS EXTANT WHEN BURDETT SURVEYED CHESHIRE 1772-1774

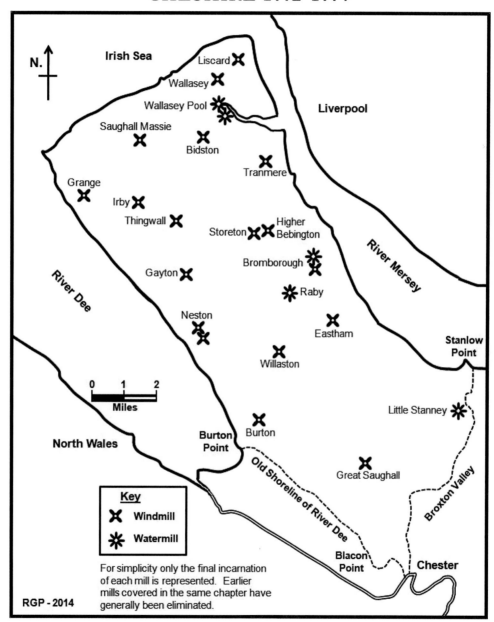

5. The windmills and watermills extant when Burdett surveyed Cheshire and covered in Part 2.

As stated in the Introduction, every mill which existed at the time of Peter Burdett's survey, or that was built after that date, is given a section of its own within Part 2. These mills are ordered geographically within four chapters, each covering a different area of the peninsula. First the mills of north Wirral are considered, before moving on to those mills on the Dee side of the peninsula. Then the mills of the peninsula's Mersey side are examined and the final chapter considers the mills of south Wirral. Some mills could relevantly have been placed in multiple chapters, but the structure used maintains a similar number of mills per chapter. Order within a chapter is based on geographical location, starting with the mills to the north of each region, with the mills becoming progressively more southerly as each chapter progresses.

CHAPTER 3: MILLS OF NORTH WIRRAL

3.1 Liscard Mill

Liscard mill was a post mill demolished over one and a half centuries ago. For many years it was the property of the manorial lord of Liscard. John Hough was the lord of the manor of Liscard from 1752. The first known reference to the mill is in 'The Journal of John Hough' dated 1754 which records that – "We winnowed up our wheat & put 8 measures in the loft, besides a batch sent to the mill". The miller at Liscard mill in the late 1780s was John Bibby, who is described as a miller in his will dated 1778. In his will, held at Cheshire Record Office, he stated that "my will is that the house and field and the mill be sold to Discharge my said Debts and funnerall Expense". The will was signed in the presence of John Hough, who was named as one of John Bibby's executors and acted as such on his death in 1782.

Latterly the mill belonged to the Penkett family who were the last lords of the manor of Liscard. Rights were transferred to the Penketts following the death of John Hough in 1797. After his death the lordship and manor of Liscard were offered for sale in 1800. The resultant indenture of 1801 was printed in 'Further Notes on the Penkett Family' in 1920. This stated that "the executors have sold to John Penkett for £2,513 – All the Manor of Liscard...also all that close of land called Stoney hey, with the wind mill & two dwelling houses erected thereon".

The mill is mentioned several times in *The Rise and Progress of Wallasey* which describes the location thus – "Liscard Mill stood in the field on the East side of the narrow footpath which connected Earlston Road with Mount Pleasant Road, parallel to Kirkway on the east side". Liscard mill is first shown on Burdett's *Chart of the Harbour of Liverpool* dated 1771. It is then shown on Burdett's map of Cheshire published in 1777, Greenwood's map of 1819 and Bryant's map of 1831. However, it had been demolished by the early 1840s, for it does not feature on the Liscard township tithe map of c.1841. The field name for plot 268 on the tithe map is "Mill Field", so there are clear indications that there was a mill in that vicinity. Burdett's chart provides the earliest known cartographic reference for this mill, but it was already of some age at that point. The structure was likely at least 17th century in origin.

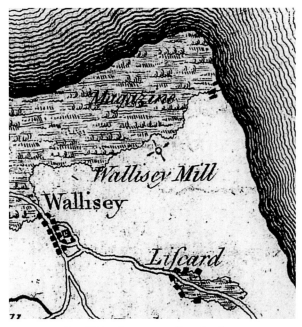

6. Liscard mill is shown on Burdett's map, although Burdett marked this mill as "Wallisey Mill".

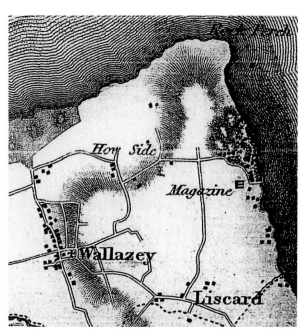

7. Greenwood's map records a basic road network, not shown by Burdett's map. The symbol for a windmill appears above and to the left of the word "Magazine".

Writing in 'The Old Flour Mills of Wirral', Mitford Abraham mentioned a post mill which stood "at the top of Mount Pleasant Road" in reference to Liscard mill. Writing in 1903 he said – "This mill was pulled down about seventy years ago, but is still remembered as an extremely antiquated concern by a few old Wallasey residents. A millstone lay near the site until a few years since."

This would mean that Mitford Abraham placed the demolition of the mill in the early 1830s, probably not so many years after the publication of Bryant's map. This seems a reasonable assumption for it does not feature on any maps after Bryant's and is not shown on the first edition Ordnance Survey map of c.1840. Williams and Crompton in their 'Windmills of Wirral' suggested that the mill was demolished "in 1833, about the time when Mount Pleasant Road was being laid out near the site". For a millstone to have existed so many decades after the mill's demolition, as seen by Mitford Abraham, sounds quite a survival, especially when one considers the mass urbanisation of the area which occurred in the early 20th century. I would assume that this was why this relic eventually disappeared.

The exact site of this mill is uncertain. Bryant's map of 1831 shows the mill some way east of the junction of Mount Pleasant Road and Mount Road. On the other hand, Greenwood's map shows the mill directly south of this road junction. To try and pinpoint the position at which Liscard mill stood on the modern terrain is extremely difficult. It is so long since this mill disappeared that it is only shown on early maps of Cheshire and it does not appear on any Ordnance Survey maps. These early maps give the approximate position of the mill and are useful for showing that it existed at a certain time. However, the surveys for the maps were not necessarily conducted to great accuracy and so they do not always show precise locations. It is certain that this mill once stood on the southern side of Mount Pleasant Road, in the vicinity of the Mount Road crossroads. The area today is so far removed from the rural landscape of which Liscard mill was a part, that it is difficult to say precisely where.

3.2 Wallasey Mill

For some centuries, a windmill stood on the high sandstone outcrop known as "the Breck" in Wallasey. The Kingston survey of 1665 shows a post mill on the Breck, south of the village of Wallasey. It is not known how long a mill had existed here for up until that point. A mill is also marked in this area of Wallasey on Collins's survey of the River Dee published in 1689. It is not clear if the mill shown is Wallasey mill, or Poulton mill which is mentioned in Part 3, as that would also have existed at this time. The Wallasey post mill was later replaced by a three storey tower mill of the typical local style, which stood south of St. Hilary's church, on the other side of St. Hilary Brow. This mill was built using local sandstone in 1765 and was a fairly early example of a tower mill on Wirral. It had no stage and Williams and Crompton noted that the endless chain used to rotate the cap could "be fastened to a ring of diagonally fixed cleats near the base of the tower". This little stone mill was one of Wirral's most aesthetically pleasing windmills, but it ceased to work during the early 1880s.

Wallasey mill is clearly marked on Bryant's map of 1831, yet it is not shown on Burdett's map of 1777 or Greenwood's map of 1819. It undoubtedly existed at both these dates, but was erroneously missed from the surveys. A mill marked "Wallisey Mill" on Burdett's map of 1777 is not this mill, but is in fact Liscard mill. The mill is shown on the Wallasey township tithe map of c.1842, which lists a "windmill and yard" occupying the relevant plot. At this time the tithe apportionment shows the owner and occupier of the mill to have been James Meadows, who was presumably the miller. By 1864 the miller seems to have been William Lee, who was listed as such in *Morris & Co.'s Directory of Cheshire* of that date. The last miller was probably Peter Joynson, who was listed at "Wallasey mill" in *Slater's Directory of Cheshire and Liverpool* dated 1883. He had been working the mill from at least 1878.

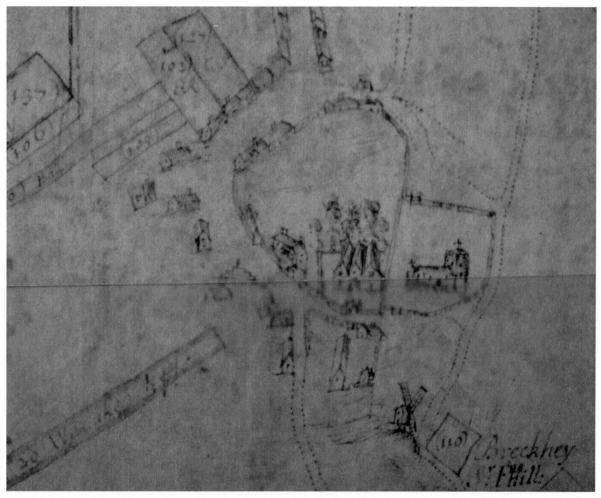

8. The Kingston survey marks windmills with a small sketch of a post mill, and provides the earliest known drawings of windmills on Wirral. Here, Wallasey mill is drawn beneath a sketch of St. Hilary's Church. (Courtesy of Cheshire Archives and Local Studies)

9. Bryant's map marks this mill to the south of Wallasey
village and near to the old Wallasey Grammar School.

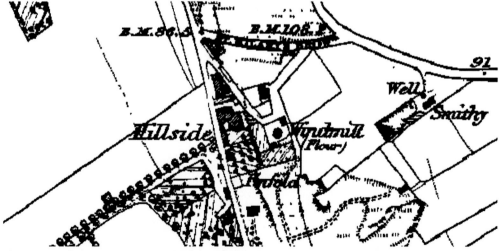

10. The Ordnance Survey map of c.1875 marks the access track which formerly led to Wallasey mill
from the junction of St. Hilary Brow and Breck Road. (Courtesy of and Copyright Old-Maps and
Ordnance Survey)

Writing in the early 20th century a Wallasey resident who remembered the mill at work reminisced – "as a child I remember going there to buy flour. We lived in the end house just across the lane. In one's childish mind the sails held a fascination. As in imagination we held on to the ends, we fancied ourselves whirled round and round as they worked to grind the flour. Suddenly letting go we would be flung far out onto the marshes. One very stormy night the sails broke loose and went racing round at a terrific speed. Our father was awakened and hurried across to help the miller. I believe they were just in time to avert a fire". This story was reproduced in *The Wirral Journal* in 1982 and serves as a reminder that fire was a continuous threat to windmills as a whole, especially where the machinery was wooden. More than one of Wirral's mills was burned down when the sails broke loose.

11. This old photograph of Wallasey mill could be as early as the later 1860s. It shows the mill in full working order, with sailcloths in place upon the common sails. St. Hilary's Church may be seen to the right. (Courtesy of Ian Boumphrey)

12. This oil painting by James Henry Robinson is dated 1884, which was around the time that Wallasey mill ceased to work. (Courtesy of the Williamson Art Gallery and Museum)

14. *Wallasey mill in the early 1880s, as seen from common land on the Breck. To the right is a rocky outcrop left by quarrying operations, known locally as the "Granny Rock" and still extant today. (Courtesy of Ian Boumphrey)*

13. *Wallasey mill in the early 1880s, as seen from the walled yard which surrounded the tower. A row of cleats may be seen near the bottom of the mill, as used to hold the chain which would have turned the cap. (Courtesy of the Mills Archive Trust)*

15. *This photograph shows Wallasey mill around the mid-1880s, by which point it had already ceased to operate. (Courtesy of Ian Boumphrey)*

16. *Wallasey mill is seen on the Breck, probably in the 1880s. The wheel used to rotate the cap is silhouetted especially clearly. (Courtesy of Birkenhead Reference Library)*

After it had fallen out of use the mill was bought by George Peers, who demolished the building in 1887. Noël E. Smith, writing in *Almost an Island* said that Peers "wanted to make the old mill into a residence, but it was unsuitable, so it was knocked down". After the demolition Peers constructed his house on the site of the old mill; a brick built mansion which was named Millthwaite. Millthwaite had a central tower, which was purportedly built on the very same spot which the mill had formerly occupied. In addition, Mitford Abraham said that "The wooden gates to this house are built out of the old arms [sails] of the mill". Millthwaite sounds to have been a most interesting house but unfortunately this too was demolished. It became unoccupied and was pulled down in the name of redevelopment in 1968. Since then a block of flats called Millthwaite Court have been built on the land; they are drab and uninteresting compared to both of the other buildings which have occupied this site.

Even today the site of Wallasey mill is identifiable. The road name Millthwaite Road, dating from when the house Millthwaite stood here, hints that there was once a mill in the area. A little way along Millthwaite Road stands the brick built block of flats, Millthwaite Court, which occupy the mill's site. An old sandstone wall partially encircles the flats and probably used to surround the mill property. The tithe map shows the mill to have been within a walled enclosure. The access track to the mill which ran up the Breck from the junction of Breck Road and St. Hilary Brow still exists. It starts as a rough downhill path in the car park of Millthwaite Court and eventually joins the driveway for a house at which point it is retained by sandstone walls.

17. Millthwaite Court in 2008; this block of flats occupies the site of Wallasey mill.

3.3 Saughall Massie Mill

There used to be a post mill in Saughall Massie, just north of the main village and originally belonging to the Earl of Derby. A windmill existed here in the 16th century and Brownbill in his 'A History of the Old Parish of Bidston, Cheshire' relates that "In 1598 John and Henry Bennett purchased from William earl of Derby the windmill and 30 ac. of land in Saugham Massie". Another reference in the same year may be found in the plea rolls for the County of Chester, where in September 1598 John Bennett took action against the Earl of Derby regarding the windmill here. Brownbill found no earlier reference in the Derby rental of 1521-1522. This mill is marked on the Kingston survey of the Manor of Bidston dated 1665, which shows a road linking it to a triangular village green. But it was not a component of the Bidston estate, for it was privately owned, possibly by the Bennetts.

It is unknown when the last mill on this site dated from, for it may have been a rebuilt structure. The final structure was once the property of the Vyner family, who owned the mill from at least 1719. Brownbill stated that Esther Martin was the occupier in 1719 with the rent being £6 per annum. The Vyners' 1762 valuation documents show that Thomas Kirk was renting the mill at that point. The mill is marked on Burdett's map of 1777. Earlier 18th century cartographic reference is provided by Fearon and Eyes's coastal chart surveyed between 1736 and 1737; this marks the mill as "Saughon Mill". Interestingly the mill is not shown on Greenwood's map of 1819 even though it existed at that time; it must have been missed off the original survey for it was added on to the revised edition of 1830. Saughall Massie mill is also shown on Bryant's map of 1831.

18. Bryant's map clearly marks Saughall Massie mill as "The Mill".
It also shows the Mill House to the north.

Many famous Wallasey smuggling stories centre on an old inn known as "Mother Redcap's". Mother Redcap played a key part in local smuggling legend, for much contraband was purportedly hidden on her premises. Smuggled goods needed to be transported to the other side of Bidston Moss for sale. If it was reported that it was not safe to proceed directly across the moss to Bidston then the contraband was reputedly taken along the western edge of Bidston Moss, for storage in Saughall Massie mill.

For this reason Joseph Kitchingman included an account of the mill in his 'Notes on Mother Redcap's'. Kitchingman's account was later included in *The Rise and Progress of Wallasey* and states that: - "The old mill at Saughall Massie stood about a mile from the village. It was a most remarkable structure, with strong oak beams and gaunt, primitive sails, standing alone on a rough base of stone, with a large wheel to turn the wooden mill around on the ground. The mill stood entirely by itself a little way from the edge of the moss. Secret meetings of various kinds, political and otherwise, were held in the old mill, which was away from civilization. It was supposed to be haunted, and there were ravens in it." This description suggests that this mill was probably a turret type post mill, or a tripod post mill with its substructure elevated upon stone plinths.

This mill is marked on the tithe map of c.1842, which shows how the mill was situated near to a distinctive bend in the road. On the plot description, Richard Hale is listed as the occupier. The Hales were an old milling family who worked several of the peninsula's windmills. Richard Hale was one of the last millers at Saughall Massie mill. He is listed as a corn miller there in *William's Commercial Directory of Chester* dated 1846 and also in *White's Cheshire Directory* of 1860. This mill must have ceased to work at some point in the 1860s and was probably destroyed in the early 1870s. It is not shown on the Ordnance Survey map of c.1875 as by that point it had already been demolished.

In 1903 Mitford Abraham said that the site could "still be seen near the south corner of a field". He went on to say that "The old Saughal Massie mill was rented for the last few years by a man named Massey. His wife, who still lives in the village, said in a pathetic way that the mill was the ruin of her husband, and was not pulled down, but actually fell to pieces". Mitford Abraham also stated that after the mill ceased to work "The ruins were sold, and a portion of the works, with one pair of stones were taken to Bidston Hall and worked as a steam mill in an outbuilding there for about twenty years. This pair of stones is still to be seen lying outside." Over a century later these heavy millstones may still be in the vicinity of Bidston Hall.

The mill house, which was the miller's former home, still existed in Mitford Abraham's time, along with "an old lane, partly lined with packhorse stones" which had once connected the house and the mill. The mill house is still marked on Ordnance Survey maps up until c.1910, but was demolished soon afterwards, and there are no remaining traces of it today. The road name Millhouse Lane is now the only existing reminder of that building. The site of Saughall Massie mill itself is smothered by modern housing. The mill was situated at the bend in the road now known as Acton Lane, but there is nothing there to see. This is perhaps not too surprising, considering how urbanised this area has become in the one hundred and forty years since this mill's demolition.

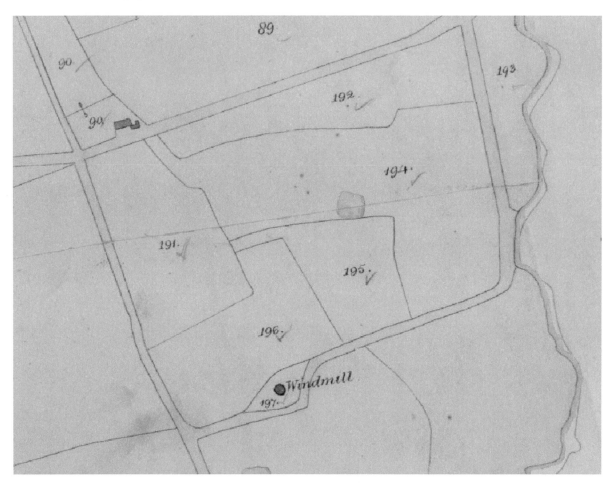

19. The tithe map of c.1842 of Saughall Massie township demonstrates how this mill was situated at a distinctive kink in the road. (Courtesy of Cheshire Archives and Local Studies)

3.4 Wallasey Pool Mills

Two watermills formerly existed on Wallasey Pool, that tidal inlet of the River Mersey, now forming Birkenhead Docks and entirely surrounded by urbanisation. These mills were located at the westerly end of the pool and entirely disappeared in the early 19th century. During the time of their existence they were isolated in rural surroundings. They operated prior to the rise of other industries in the area, and had gone by the time other major industry arrived. These mills appear to have been known as the Pool mills, Bidston mills and the Moss mills, all of which have been used to describe them at various times.

Both mills are marked on Burdett's map of 1777, but they are not shown on Greenwood's map of 1819, by which point they had already stopped working. A second map which shows these mills is Hunter's map of 1810. However, this map appears to be heavily based upon Burdett's survey, which was updated so as to show the Ellesmere Canal. It seems unlikely that much new survey work was carried out in this corner of Wirral and these mills may well have been out of use even when the map was first published. It would seem that the mills existed from at least 1745, for they are mentioned in the Wallasey parish registers of that year and were operated by John Penkett. The date at which they first appeared was probably somewhat earlier in the 18th century. John Penkett died in 1758 and the mills were advertised for sale the following year. They were not sold, nor were they when advertised for a second time in 1760. Both mills passed to John's brother, William Penkett, who still ran them in 1765. The mills were apparently leased to William Penkett at £36 15s. a year, a large sum at that time, but by whom it is not known. William Penkett was an eminent businessman with many concerns in the local area; he died in 1785, but the mills evidently continued to work further into the late 18th century. The parish registers record James Talbot there in 1797. It has been suggested that the mills worked until at least 1803, the year his lease expired.

Due to their close proximity to the tidal waters of Wallasey Pool, these mills were successfully operated as tide mills. Of the several sorts of tide mill, one type would capture the tidal waters within a mill pool as the tide came in. These waters could then be released and the watermill worked in the conventional manner using the water obtained from the rising tide. These tide mills on Wallasey Pool are thought to have worked on this principle. The flood tide was impounded in a pool, or multiple pools, and then used to supply several waterwheels. These mills were no small scale business venture. They are purported to have occupied a frontage of some thirty six yards and extended eight yards in breath, whilst standing four storeys tall.

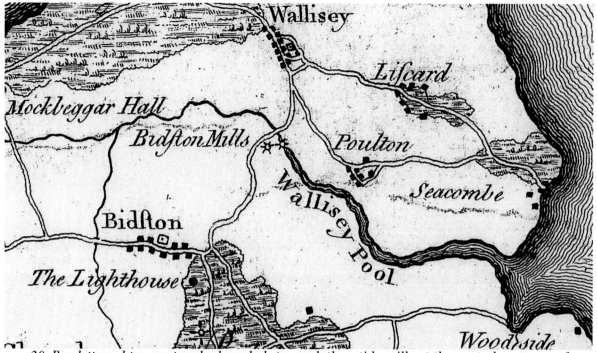

20. Burdett used two waterwheel symbols to mark these tide mills at the westerly extreme of Wallasey Pool. They are labelled as "Bidston Mills".

The primary function of one of the mills was a slitting mill for the processing of wrought iron, the only one of Wirral's mills related to an industry other than flour milling. According to Woods writing 'Further Notes on the Penkett Family', the 1745 reference to the mills in Wallasey parish registers records John Penkett as a "slitter of iron at Bidston". This slitting mill was worked by two waterwheels, each eighteen feet in diameter and produced rod and hoop iron from raw material. Rod iron consisted of iron bars, whilst hoop iron was flattened strips formed by passing the wrought iron through rollers. Eric Rideout, who discovered a contemporary account of the mills, made some notes which were printed with Woods's notes on the Penketts. Rideout remarked that – "There were two furnaces with cutters and rollers, and other apparatus for making hoops and dealing with rod iron. The capacity was stated to be eighteen tons of rod iron per week, and in addition the plant could slit and roll five tons of hoops in the same period". This is an impressive output for the period and in terms of industry on Wirral, this sort of activity was otherwise entirely unknown.

The second mill was a flour mill. Other accounts have tended to assume that this was a secondary concern in comparison to that of iron slitting. Marriott writing in *Cheshire Life* in 1952 wrote that "Incidentally, there was a small corn mill nearby, for the staff of the tidal mill constituted a self-contained community". In reality it would seem that this mill produced flour on an almost industrial scale, in a manner quite dissimilar to the local mills commonly found on Wirral. It was every bit as important as the slitting mill, possibly even more so. When the mills were advertised in Williamson's *Liverpool Advertiser* of 23rd February 1759, the corn mill was mentioned first, for the advertisement ran – "a large set of Tide Water Cornmills at Bidston…Also an Iron Slitting Mill situate and worked by the said Pool…Also seven dwelling houses etc." The flour mill was said to be worked by four waterwheels eighteen feet in diameter. The power output of this many waterwheels would have been quite considerable. Tidal power allowed the mill to work an average of fourteen hours every day.

Rideout's account of the grain mill states that – "The corn mill consisted of three double rolling mills and three single ones, with fans and screens. In addition there was a machine for screening black wheat. There were also two kilns for drying oats. With this plant it was possible to turn out 250 quarters of wheat, and to roll and grind 200 quarters of oats in six days. For the period, 1759, the equipment appears to have been excellent". This must certainly have been the largest water powered milling concern ever to operate on Wirral. The reference to the mills as "rolling mills" is intriguing, all of the other mills mentioned in this book ground grain using traditional millstones. In the third volume of their *History of Corn Milling* Bennett and Elton provided an appendix covering the history of roller milling. They suggested that when rollers first appeared as a means of milling flour, they were very inefficient and quite ineffective in comparison to standard millstones. In 1753 Isaac Wilkinson, a Lancashire ironmaster, took out a patent for "a new sort of cast metallick rolls for crushing, flattening, bruising or grinding malt, oats, beans, or any kind of grain". It is not known how he intended his rolls to be powered. Another patent taken out in 1774, of a similar nature, was for rolls which were to be turned by hand. Bennett and Elton thought that the first attempt to build mills with powered rollers was in 1820, at various locations in continental Europe. Wallasey Pool mills stopped working almost two decades before that. Perhaps this corn mill represented a significant investment, to trial a new piece of technology, but ultimately proved unsustainable.

There was also a small settlement built around these mills, as shown by the 1759 advertisement, which mentions that there were seven cottages. One of these was "fit for a manager to live in". Other buildings included storage facilities, from which flour was sold, a carpenter's shop, stables and a dovecot. This quantity of buildings would have formed a small hamlet; although Rideout was unable to ascertain "Whether this small town was all collected on the marshes, together with the twelve acres of 'fine pasture', or whether some dwellings were situated further afield". Entries in the Wallasey parish registers suggest that a number of people could have lived at the mills, for example "Thos. Grant of Bidston Slitting Mills", whose baby was baptised in 1762. There was evidently much scope for transport via Wallasey Pool, which was apparently navigable even by quite large vessels, able to carry one hundred tons. It seems surprising that such craft could reach the mills considering Burdett marks them well inland, at the pool's most western extent. A river flat of the more modest capacity, thirty five tons, was used to convey flour from the mills and grain to them.

These mills had already been leased to somebody else before William Penkett died in 1785. Indeed they seem to have frequently changed hands in the latter years of the 18th century. Williamson's *Liverpool Advertiser* of 10th December 1777, records that the mills were then operated by "Rigby and Crooks". This firm may have used the mills for other purposes, as well as iron slitting and flour milling, for according to their advertisement "Bidstone Mills are now working in all their branches, viz: - slitting, rolling and tilting of iron and steel, rasping and chipping of dyeing woods, manufacture of tobacco stems…and grinding of corn…Bar iron, rod iron, hoops and rolled iron of all sizes sold at Peter Rigby's warehouse, North side of the Old Dock". This is presumably a reference to the Old Dock in Liverpool and it is assumed that the finished products were mainly conveyed to the Lancashire side of the Mersey. Another change of hands occurred in 1781 when Williamson's *Liverpool Advertiser* stated – "Brice Grant, Slitter…begs leave to inform the public that he has taken and entered upon the Slitting Mill at Bidstone in Cheshire, which he intends to work in all its branches". By all appearances the mills seem to have been a profitable enterprise and there were many businessmen willing to invest in them.

References to the mills become scarce as the end of the 18th century approaches. The *Cheshire Sheaf* of August 1898 says "the Moss-mills…existed for many years during the last century and beginning of this one on the Wallasey-marsh". Neilson says in his *Auld Lang Syne* that "It is evident from the parish records, that a mill once existed on the Moss, and is referred to in the farm account books of Mr. Thomas Wharton in the year 1806". From this we can gather that the land in the area surrounding the mills was still very much agricultural. It seems strange that industry such as iron processing should be associated with the area at this early date. Raw wrought iron to process, along with grain, was evidently brought up Wallasey Pool in vast quantities. However, it is unclear why the place chosen to process this material was in such an isolated position, on the edge of Bidston Moss?

The demise of these mills is also something of a mystery. They must have been a major economic venture and the large sum of rent concerned with their lease suggests that they were a great asset to the 18th century entrepreneur. One would have thought that such a business would have continued operating longer than it seems to have done. Yet, the mills disappeared from the local news under sixty years after they entered it. The equipment they contained must have been of considerable value itself and this was presumably sold after closure. A possible reason for their eventual disappearance is given by a local notice published around the time of the final sale of the mills. This was discovered by Rideout and stated that "This is a notice that the landowners in Bidstone parish will not allow any flood gates to be set in the water course that runs through Mr Warrington's bridge. Any person that attempts to set either clough or flood gates will be proceeded against according to law". This notice seems to concern arguments over the blockage of the River Birket which was crossed by Warrington's bridge. Rideout concluded that maybe these disputes "eventually led to the abandonment of the enterprise".

Near the turn of the 20th century the mills had already gone; Mitford Abraham wrote in 1903 "The site of the mill can still be seen, and a few large stones lying about are all that remains of the building, which was pulled down nearly a century ago". It would seem that most of the buildings were demolished soon after closure, leaving little trace of this major industrial operation. It also appears that local memory of the business must have faded quickly. Indeed, such was the isolated location of these mills that perhaps there were few to remember them. Either way, previously published accounts of the mills have not necessarily grasped the extent of this endeavour. Based on the vagueness of his account it would appear that Mitford Abraham was unable to discover much information on this location.

Speaking of remains at the site of the mills Mitford Abraham said "the small whitewashed cottage still standing there was most probably the mill house". Likewise, writing around 1926 Rideout remarked that "The old whitewashed cottage, recently demolished, which stood on the Marsh…surrounded by a few feeble trees, was said to have been the miller's cottage". It is almost unbelievable that around a century after closure a sole cottage was the only reminder of this hive of activity, which must have employed many people. This could have been any one of the cottages which are said to have formed a settlement around the mills. There is a building shown on Bryant's map of 1831 as "Moss Cottage" and also on the first edition Ordnance Survey map and marked "Moss House"; this is one of the only houses shown on Bidston Moss and it is probably the same building. The building continued to be marked on Ordnance Survey maps up until c.1910. Woods and Brown writing in *The Rise and Progress of Wallasey* mentioned a moated farm house on the moss, once used by smugglers as a hiding place from authority. In 1927 Woods writing on 'Smuggling in Wirral' mentioned a possible connection between this house and the mills – "a farm house, probably at one time part of the Bidston Mills, afterwards known as Hanna Mutches".

The most reliable map these mills are known to feature on is Burdett's map of 1777, which shows two watermills beside one another. They appear to be situated on the River Birket at the western extremity of Wallasey Pool and are labelled "Bidston Mills". The road layout of Burdett's map is so far removed from that today that it is hard to say where the mills were situated. Burdett marked the mills near to a point where the River Birket is crossed by a road running between Bidston and Wallasey. Even as early as 1819 this road seems to have disappeared, for it is not shown on Greenwood's map. The area is now so extensively altered and developed that one could not possibly pinpoint the site of the mills based on only Burdett's survey.

The only known photographs of this site are two views taken by Mitford Abraham around the turn of the 20th century. These are in the possession of The Heswall Society and show the cottage previously mentioned, alongside a tidal pool. Mitford Abraham's notes with his photographs say that the pool was drained by Bidston Golf Club in 1911 and that most of the site was later overlain by Bidston Dock in the 1930s. Wallasey Pool mills lay on Bidston Moss, probably somewhere near the west end of the now in-filled Bidston Dock. However, I have been unsuccessful in my attempts to accurately locate the position of these mills; their surface remains are certainly non-existent.

21. The site of the tide mills on Wallasey Pool, as depicted in Mitford Abraham's photograph of 1901.
The old cottage, said to be related to these mills, can be seen standing alongside a pool.
(Courtesy of The Heswall Society)

3.5 Bidston Mill

A post mill stood on Bidston Hill from at least 1596, at which date a mill is mentioned in a lease from Margaret the Countess and William the Earl of Derby. Bidston manor house, park and windmill were let to William Lusher for 21 years; although the Earl of Derby's bailiff had repossessed the estate by 1597. Brownbill found no mention of the mill in the Derby rental of 1521-1522, but nor is it mentioned in the Kingston rental of 1665 at which point it certainly existed, so this is not proof against its existence. Despite no mention in the rental itself the post mill is clearly drawn upon the Kingston survey of 1665, the earliest cartographic source to show this mill. The second known reference to a mill on Bidston Hill is a document of 1609 in the Harleian Manuscripts. Irvine's abstract of this document, printed in *Wirral Notes and Queries*, lists the annual rent payable to the Early of Derby for the Bidston estate. The manuscript is an agreement drawn up for the rental of Bidston Hall and estate, from Richard Kellie to William Fells of Arrowe. This lease included "all the parke and lande called Bidston Parke, etc., and the Wyndmillne standing on the east side of the said parke upon the Comons".

22. The Kingston survey includes a map of the former Deer Park on Bidston Hill. The post mill is marked outside the park boundary and can be seen in the margin of the map, to the right of this extract. (Courtesy of Cheshire Archives and Local Studies)

There were also some even earlier mills at Bidston, record of which may be found in a plea roll of 1357. This has been published by The Record Society of Lancashire and Cheshire, as *Cheshire Forest Eyre Roll 1357*. The roll mentions that a mill was built at Bidston in 1352 or 1353, at which point "Henry duke of Lancaster…through his bailiffs took six green oaks in Bidston wood and three in Wooton wood and an oak in Birkenhead wood for building a mill at Bidston in le Thwayt without the view of the foresters; and that timber from the old mill [*antiqui molendini*] was sold to Richard del Hogh". Trees on Wirral were protected by forest law, and the felling of these ten trees to construct a mill constituted an offence. The location "in le Thwayt" uses "thwaite", a term of Scandinavian origin meaning "clearing", so this mill evidently stood in a cleared area.

Historical records of thwaites in Bidston generally seem to have referred to an area of cleared land on the west side of Bidston Moss. The tithe map of c.1842 shows a group of ten fields, all bearing names including "Thwaite", on and to the north of what is now Bidston Golf Club. This could well be the portion of the township where a mill was built c.1353. The River Birket runs nearby, so the first mills at Bidston could have been watermills, for the type of mill is not explicitly stated in the eyre. However, it is highly probable, especially in light of the early rebuilding c.1353, that these mills were medieval post mills. If so, the first mill to stand in the thwaite could have been amongst Wirral's earliest windmills, and was probably very lightly constructed. If these early windmills were situated near the edge of Bidston Moss, the site cannot have been an especially favourable one for catching the wind. This is presumably why a radical change of site later took place, a position on the hilltop having been adopted by the end of the 16th century.

Another early reference to the post mill on Bidston Hill in the Derby muniments is a bill of complaint filed in 1620 and reproduced in the *Cheshire Sheaf* of February 1953. Further 17th century reference comes from the 'Sequestrators' Accounts for Wirral' published in the *Cheshire Sheaf* in 1955. These tell us that in 1644 John Ordes was paying the Earl of Derby £1 10s. for a quarter year's rent of Bidston mill. In 1646 the Earl of Derby paid £1 3s. for "Repairing Bidston Milne in boardes and nayles and putting up a sayle rodd". Writing in his 'A History of the Old Parish of Bidston, Cheshire' Brownbill mentions a Derby rental where the mill has been listed under the chief rents for Bidston and then crossed out. He concluded that "it may be inferred that at some time after 1656 the lord of the manor had sold the mill, or milling rights".

Certainly by 1758 the Vyner family owned the windmill. At this date Robert Vyner leased the mill, along with Bidston Hall and other land, to Thomas Watmough of Bidston for twenty three years. The post mill remained in the hands of the Vyners until 1791 when a strong gale caused the sails to break loose. They spun at such speed that the wooden mill was set on fire, through heat generated by the resultant friction, and burnt to the ground. Burdett's map of 1777 predated the construction of the present tower mill, and he marked the old post mill on an area labelled as "Bidston Heath". The post mill is also shown on Collins's survey of the River Dee, published in 1689 and surveyed earlier in the 1680s.

Other 18th century charts marking the post mill are Fearon and Eyes's survey published in 1738, on which the windmill is clearly marked "Bidston Mill" and Williamson's chart of 1766.

23. Burdett showed Bidston post mill on his survey, marked in an area named as "Bidston Heath".

Evidence of the old post mill may still be seen, despite the passage of two centuries since its destruction. It stood only a short distance to the north of the present mill. The foundations, into which the crosstree assembly fitted, were cut into the sandstone of Bidston Hill. In 1903 Mitford Abraham wrote of these foundations and said they took the form of – "two trenches about 15 feet long by 3 feet wide, dug out of the solid rock, and shaped like a Greek cross. These trenches which were about two feet deep, cross each other at right angles, and are now nearly filled up with earth". A century later this feature is less obvious, yet it can still be made out. Other remains exist too; at one point two rectangular depressions have been cut into the rock. These are reputed to have held some kind of locking mechanism for the mill's tailpole. At another point there is a row of footholds carved into the hill; the miller could have improved his grip using these, as he pushed the mill around. In 1976 Williams and Crompton claimed that it was possible to see "a circular groove, 61ft. in diameter, worn by the tail-pole".

The present mill at Bidston superseded the old post mill following its destruction. It is a three storey, brick built tower mill, thirty three feet tall, and was constructed in the very early 19th century. The mill has three small windows, although Williams and Crompton suggested that "others may be hidden under the cement rendering". For most of its working life Bidston mill had a cap rotated by an endless chain, which passed over a chain wheel. Intriguingly however, when the mill was first constructed the cap was turned using a tailpole, the only definite example of a tailpole on one of Wirral's tower mills. A wheel was affixed to the end of this tailpole which rested upon the ground. This setup is clearly shown by the painting, *Bidstone Light House and Signals*, at the Williamson Art Gallery. The painting is by Henry F. James and is thought to date from c.1807. The mill was presumably built this way, and was updated by the provision of a chain wheel later on, at an unknown date. The top of Bidston Hill is very exposed and mills here were particularly vulnerable during storms. There were several occasions when the sails on this tower mill broke free. On at least two occasions the fires generated completely destroyed the sails and internal machinery. These fires occurred in 1821 and 1839; it could be that a tailpole remained in use at Bidston until the first fire. Much of the original machinery remains in place and this presumably dates to some point after the second fire.

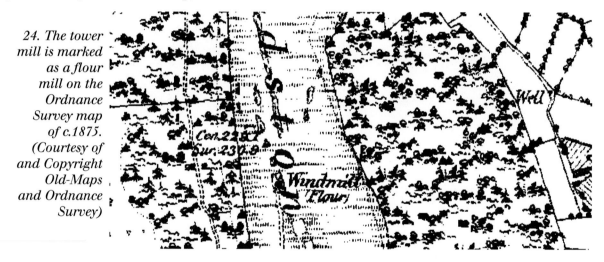

24. The tower mill is marked as a flour mill on the Ordnance Survey map of c.1875. (Courtesy of and Copyright Old-Maps and Ordnance Survey)

Bidston mill was difficult to access and was a fairly early, Victorian closure, for it stopped working c.1875. Neilson writing in *Auld Lang Syne* said "The old mill's working days terminated through a break-down of the machinery that turned the great round grinding stone". So it seems possible that the mill was forced out of action following a mechanical problem. Windmills were dangerous buildings and one of Bidston's millers was tragically killed, having been hit on the head by the revolving sails. Neilson said that – "Once a venturesome youth, one of a Birkenhead pic-nic party, out of bravado grasped one of the mill sails as they were slowly revolving, fully intending to let go before being carried too far, but he lost his nerve and failed to let go…Fortunately, the miller was able to stop the mill and lower him down". By all accounts, he had a lucky escape.

Between 1894 and 1908 Bidston Hill was bought from the Vyner family. The money needed was raised by the Corporation of Birkenhead and by public subscription. To accompany the opening of the hill to the public the windmill was restored in 1894, using money provided by Robert Hudson, the soap manufacturer. The windmill historian Rex Wailes believed that Bidston mill was the first mill in the country to be intentionally preserved. By the time of restoration the mill was in a ruinous condition, with only one sail and part of the cap remaining. Having funded the restoration Robert Hudson took the single original sail which remained on the mill, along with another which had blown down. According to Mitford Abraham it was his intention to have chairs made out of these. Although the mill's exterior had suffered from years of neglect, much of the original machinery remained inside. This too was restored to a presentable condition and fortunately remains to this day. This machinery is the last remaining from any of Wirral's once numerous windmills. The long term preservation of this mill may not have occurred; its current state is largely down to the foresight of the Vyner family. According to Neilson – "When the mill ceased to function and became vacant many applications were received by caterers who wished to convert and run it as a tea house or café. These applications were most fortunately declined by Mr Vyner".

25. Here, Bidston mill is seen from the opposite side of Vyner Road North in 1892, prior to its restoration in 1894. (Courtesy of The Heswall Society)

26. Bidston mill in a derelict state and with only two sails remaining in 1892. It had not been used since around 1875. (Courtesy of the Mills Archive Trust)

27. Bidston mill as photographed in 1894, shortly before the commencement of its restoration in the same year. (Courtesy of Ian Boumphrey)

28. This photograph of 1899 shows Bidston mill in a fine condition, five years after its restoration. (Courtesy of the Mills Archive Trust)

29. A severe storm in 1927 blew the cap and sails from Bidston mill. This photograph shows repairs being carried out afterwards. (Courtesy of the Mills Archive Trust)

Bidston mill is the only surviving tower mill on Wirral which retains all of its interior features. As such, it is an important survivor. Internally it has a lot in common with the rest of Wirral's tower mills, many of which have now been lost. It serves to remind us how things were in numerous other cases. In 1927 a severe storm blew off the entire cap along with all four sails; further restoration was undertaken to repair the mill. The sails were replaced again during the 1970s. In 2006 another restoration project was begun, in order to repair the mill's cap. This involved the replacement of a lot of material which was in poor condition. The mill was closed to the public in 2003. Since then £120,000 has been spent and the interior brought up to current safety standards. The mill re-opened to the public in April 2009.

On the ground floor of the mill a horizontal shaft is connected to the flour dresser. The flour dresser sifted out flour of a certain grade by removing larger items such as bran, left behind by the milling process. In the 1930s a visitor to the mill recorded that at ground level traces could once be seen of former windows and most interestingly a second doorway into the mill on the northern side. These original features are said to have been destroyed during restoration. Other items visible on the ground floor are two governors which are coupled to each set of millstones on the floor above. These were used to regulate the speed of the stones individually. The first floor is the stone floor where two pairs of millstones may be seen. The running stones are coupled to three and a half inch diameter iron shafts, driven from above by the great spur wheel which lies between the first and second floors. This great spur wheel is of wooden clasp arm construction, with cast iron teeth.

The floor above the stone floor is the bin floor. On this floor there were hoppers, designed to feed the millstones below with grain. The remains of the sack hoist are present, although only the main framework and bearing are extant. This hoist was driven by a cast iron bevel gear beneath the floor, which remains in place. A central feature of this floor is the vertical main shaft, twenty two inches square, which connects the great spur wheel to the wallower. The wallower itself is housed on the next level, directly beneath the cap. It is made of wood and is of clasp arm construction, but is fitted with cast iron teeth, like the great spur wheel. The brake wheel which would have connected the wallower to the sails is now missing, but the cast iron windshaft, to which the sails are affixed, can still be seen. The top wall of the tower has a cast iron rack gear attached in sections, part of the mechanism used to turn the cap. A set of iron reduction gears are engaged with this rack and these connect to the chain wheel on the mill's exterior.

30. Seen from inside the tower mill, one sail of which is visible, the in-filled and grassy cross in the foreground denotes the site of Bidston's post mill.

31. These footholds carved into the rock of Bidston Hill would have improved the miller's grip for pushing the post mill around.

32. *The restored tower mill at Bidston as seen in 2014.*

33. *The chain wheel used to rotate the cap is clearly visible in this view of Bidston mill.*

34. *This governor on the ground floor of the mill is connected to a pair of millstones on the floor above.*

35. *The great spur wheel is situated between the first and second floors and features cast iron teeth.*

36. *A bevel gear which drove the mill's sack hoist from the great spur wheel.*

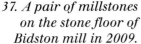

37. A pair of millstones on the stone floor of Bidston mill in 2009.

It is very lucky that Bidston mill survives in its present condition. Neilson's *Auld Lang Syne* provides a quote describing the working days of this, Wirral's most complete mill. This description would have fitted many of Wirral's windmills, in the days before the ancient craft of milling was lost. – "I distinctly remember a walk over Bidston Hill when a child with an elder sister, about the year 1868. A fresh breeze was blowing and the sails of the old mill were turning round in full swing, grinding corn. A cart laden with full sacks of flour stood just ready to leave by the stony cart-track to the road below while the miller stood talking to the carter. As we stood watching, the loaded cart moved off and the miller asked us if we would care to look inside the mill? His invitation we gladly accepted and in we went. My first and lasting impression was the loud buzzing noise of the machinery, very like the sound of a swarm of angry bees but much louder, and my next, the whiteness of everything inside the mill, caused by a coating of fine white flour dust which nothing could escape, not even the miller himself. This was Mr. Robert Youds, the last of his kind to work the old mill". This must be a reference to Robert Youde, who was listed as the miller here in *Morris & Co.'s Directory of Cheshire* of 1864.

CHAPTER 4: MILLS OF WIRRAL'S DEE SIDE

4.1 Grange Mill

There was formerly a post mill at Grange, which stood near the northern end of Caldy Hill. This sandstone outcrop is at the north end of a ridge which runs down the Dee side of the Wirral Peninsula. Due to the fact that this mill stood on a prominent hilltop, not far from the coast, it was a valuable navigational aid for mariners. For this reason the mill is clearly marked on several old sea charts; the charts show it as a sighting line for mariners navigating the Irish Sea. One of the earliest maps marking the mill is Collins's chart of 1689, which clearly shows the mill as a sighting line for ships entering the Hoyle Lake. Fearon and Eyes's chart of 1738 also shows the mill, as do Williamson's chart of 1766 and Burdett's chart of 1771. Brownbill, writing in *West Kirby and Hilbre*, said "Ships coming to Liverpool from the west would sight the windmill on Grange Hill to the south of them, and proceed to the south east, keeping the two Sea Lights in line…".

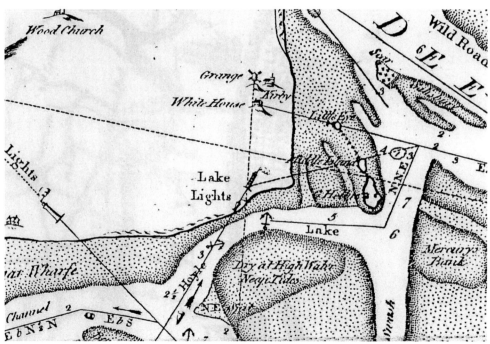

38. Burdett's chart of 1771 marks a mill at Grange and shows
it as a sighting line for ships navigating Liverpool Bay.

A mill stood at Grange in medieval times and originally belonged to the monks of Basingwerk Abbey in Flintshire. Land in the parish of West Kirby had been held by Basingwerk Abbey from 1152. It is not certain if the last mill to stand here was the original medieval structure. It seems probable that a number of mills may have stood here over the centuries. The first known reference to this mill is in Henry VIII's survey of ecclesiastical wealth, *Valor Ecclesiasticus*, carried out in the first half of 1535. Volume IV of the survey, as published by the Record Commission in 1821, records a windmill ("*molend' ventritici*") in "Westkyrby" owned by Basingwerk Abbey and worth 40s. per annum. This was Grange mill, for despite its name, it was actually in West Kirby township, adjacent to the boundary with Grange township. After the dissolution of Basingwerk Abbey in 1536, the mill here became the property of the Crown and was rented to Thomas Coventree at a rate of 40s. per year. An indenture of 1537 printed by Brownbill granted to Hugh Price for 40s. a farm, along with the "Mill of Westkirkbye…for twenty-one years beginning at the Feast of St. Michael next, together with sufficient stone to make millstones for the said mill as required; the said Hugh to carry out all necessary repairs". Another reference from 1537 is a roll from the Augmentation Office printed in *Monasticon Anglicanum*. This refers to a single windmill in West Kirby as "*unius molendi ventriciti*".

In 1551 the tenant of the mill was still Hugh Price and the mill then passed to a Robert Radcliffe, in whose will the lease of the mill is mentioned in 1569. By 1581 the mill was being leased to John Seyborne, along with his son William and daughter-in-law Katherine. The mill was purchased from the Crown by Edward Ferrers and Francis Philips in 1610. The seizure of monastic property at the time of the Dissolution of the Monasteries led to Henry VIII owning a large number of former monastic mills across the country. Many of these royal mills remained property of the Crown until the reign of James I. Ferrers and Philips, who purchased Grange mill, had formed a partnership in 1609. According to Bennett and Elton in Volume 3 of their *History of Corn Milling* "The gentlemen who seem to have specially fostered the desire of James I. to convert his milling enterprises into money were two enterprising speculators, Edward Ferrers and Francis Philips who, very rarely purchasing any property but mills, in the course of time attained the position of being the most extensive mill-owners the kingdom has ever known…purchasing them in large batches from the king, and retailing them to local speculators at a profit". In 1608, a year prior to the sale of any of his mills, James I had a list compiled of those mills in his possession. A note with the list suggests that it may not be entirely complete. There were four royal mills listed in Cheshire; one of these formerly owned by "Basingwarke Priory", was a "Windmill in West Kirby", which was valued at £2 per annum.

For many years this windmill was the property of the Glegg family of Grange, who purchased it from Ferrers and Philips at some point after 1610. They certainly held the mill by 1636; in that year William Glegg died at Grange and his inquisition post mortem of 1640 records that he had a mill in West Kirby worth 40s. The inquisition was printed in *Cheshire Inquisitions Post Mortem: Stuart Period 1603-1660*. It refers to a "fine...levied 28 April, 15 James I [1617]...he was...seised of a windmill in West Kirby, with all suits, socs, tolls, multures, &c., thereunto belonging". It was also said that William Glegg's wife Alice "survives & dwells, a widow, at Great Caldey, & occupies the lands...& also the windmill conveyed by the said William Glegg on 6 June, 5 Charles I [1629] to Gilbert & Arthur Glegge [his sons] to the use of said Alice". Another William, the last Glegg of Grange, still held the mill in 1766, although later the estate was sold when he fell into debt. James Rainford may have been the miller in the early 19th century. His occupation was given as a miller on his will of 1804 and he was said to be a resident of Grange and West Kirby.

At some point in the past, two mills may have existed alongside each other on this hilltop. John Mackay-Math's study of the River Dee was based on a survey made in 1732. In his *An Abridged Plan of the River Dee and Hyle Lake*, there are two windmills shown here under the title of "Wood Mills". Collins only drew one mill on his chart of 1689, the result of survey work in the 1680s. However, rather interestingly his chart has two names written beside the post mill sketched upon the chart. To the left of the mill it says "Grang Mill", yet above the same sketch the chart appears to say "Granywood Mill". If a further post mill did exist, it probably disappeared soon after Mackay-Math's 1732 survey, for Fearon and Eyes do not mark it on their chart of 1738, the survey work for which was completed in 1736 and 1737. This second mill could be Newbold mill mentioned in Chapter 8, or could support the potential site identified through field names in Chapter 9.

A huge gale wrecked this mill in January 1839. We can see that this must have been a truly terrible storm, for Mitford Abraham writing over sixty years later said that the gale was "still looked upon by old people as the most violent storm which has ever blown over this district". So for many decades to come this gale continued to be firmly rooted in the memories of those who witnessed it. Such was the importance of the mill as a landmark for shipping that its disappearance had an impact on those who relied on it. Recognising the loss, The Trustees of the Liverpool Docks built a new landmark in 1841, after being granted permission from the landowner, John Shaw Leigh. This new landmark was a large beacon, now called Grange Column and built from locally quarried red sandstone. The beacon stands approximately sixty feet tall and is on the site of the old mill.

Part of the length of the column is inscribed with the legend:-

"THIS COLUMN
Was Erected by The
TRUSTEES of the LIVERPOOL DOCKS
by permission of
JOHN SHAW LEIGH ESQUIRE
OWNER of the LAND
who also granted the Stone for the Erection
ANNO DOMINI
1841
as a
BEACON for MARINERS
Frequenting the
RIVER MERSEY and its VICINITY
The foundation Stone was laid
April 16th 1841
By John Shaw Leigh Esquire"

During excavations near to the site of the mill whilst the column was being constructed, some rather unusual discoveries were made. These do not seem to have been fully recorded at the time. Brown, writing on 'The Ancient Parish of West Kirby' in 1885, said – "During an excavation…in 1840 some British urns were found, made of clay of the district, which contained human bones and ashes; and under the mill which stood on the site of the column…was found a cavern, also containing some human bones, and some articles of domestic use". Certainly, such discoveries seem to point at an ancient site of considerable antiquity.

Writing in *Twixt Mersey and Dee* in 1897 Hilda Gamlin wrote – "About three years ago the gorse took fire on the hill, and in clearing it away the two millstones, with teeth for cog-wheels, were found at the foot of the monument, where one now lies; the other, rolled down the incline by some mischievous persons, is about twelve feet from the entrance to the Echo Lane, it is lightly covered with soil". This sounds as though the millstones were recovered from the wreckage of the mill and placed at the base of the column during its construction. They later became forgotten, but were rediscovered some half a century later. In 1903 Mitford Abraham said that a millstone "was rolled down the hillside into the ditch where it remained in view until lately, when the ditch was filled up and the stone covered". This is presumably the same millstone which Gamlin mentioned. The other millstone remains at the base of the column to this day, although the gears Gamlin wrote of have long since disappeared. Williams and Crompton noted that this millstone was "unusual both in its composition, of grey granite, and in its small size, 38 inches in diameter". The thickness of this millstone seems to suggest that it was probably a bed stone.

This mill is not shown on Burdett's map of 1777, or Greenwood's map of 1819, but undoubtedly existed at both those dates. Bryant's map of 1831 is probably the last to show it and marks it as "Grange Mill". On the Ordnance Survey map of c.1875 the mill had been gone for many years and the beacon is shown on its site. A building nearby in Village Road is called "Mill Cottage". The same cottage is also shown on the tithe map of c.1844, only a few years after the mill's destruction. One of the few houses in the vicinity in past years, the cottage may well have been the miller's house. The same house still stands in Village Road although nowadays it is called "Mount Cross". Opposite this cottage there is a series of steps carved into the sandstone, which lead up to Grange Column from Village Road. These may once have formed the access route to Grange mill.

39. On the Ordnance Survey map of c.1875 Grange mill has been replaced by Grange Column,
which is marked "Beacon". A cottage, "Mill Cottage", is marked nearby.
(Courtesy of and Copyright Old-Maps and Ordnance Survey)

An interesting relic of Grange mill may still exist; bizarrely parts of the mill's sails may be extant. In 1903 Mitford Abraham said "The Mill Inn, Darmonds Green, West Kirby, is named after the mill, as some of the beams of the roof were made from the old arms". The building was originally a bakery owned by John Hale. This bakery was established in 1837 and must have moved to this building a few years later. Part of the building became the Mill Inn at a later date. The Hales were a Wirral milling family, who may have worked Grange mill, or known those who did. This is presumably how they came to obtain parts of the ruined mill and use them in the construction of this building. Now a house, the former Mill Inn still stands at the junction of Darmonds Green and De Grouchy Street.

40. The entrances to John Hale's bakery and The Mill Inn in the 1880s. The sails of Grange mill are said to have been used in the construction of this building. (Courtesy of Ian Boumphrey)

41. A 2008 view of Grange Column, constructed as an alternative landmark to Grange mill.

42. A small granite millstone which remains at the base of Grange Column to this day.

4.2 Irby Mill

There was a windmill in the vicinity of Irby for many centuries and two different mill sites are known. The first mention of a mill at the initial, ancient site, was in 1291. At this date it was mentioned in the ecclesiastical taxation of Pope Nicolas IV, the reason being that it was under the ownership of St. Werburgh's Abbey in Chester. This mill stood on the southern side of Hill Bark Road and although the exact site is unknown, it was probably in the vicinity of Irby Hill quarry. Indeed, too close a proximity to the quarry workings may have been the reason for this mill's change of site. The ancient mill fell into disuse during the 18th century and a new mill was built one hundred yards further down the hill, this time on the northern side of Hill Bark Road. This later site was situated below the brow of the hill. It was more sheltered, and did not take such advantage of the prevailing winds as the ancient site did.

The ancient mill is mentioned in a rental of St. Werburgh's which was compiled in 1431-1432, Brownbill's transcription in *West Kirby and Hilbre* reads that – "The tenants of Irby, Greasby, Woodchuch and Noctorum with those of the monks in Frankby, must grind at Irby mill to the 16th measure (i.e. they gave a sixteenth of the flour to the miller as toll) and must convey millstones from Little Christleton to the said mill, and must repair the earth work of the mill as may be needful". The abbey owned land in Little Christleton and it has been suggested that a local ferruginous sandstone available there may have been suitable for millstones. The Chartulary of St. Werburgh's Abbey mentions that the monks had been given some land in Little Christleton in the 1120s.

In 1538, some years before St. Werburgh's surrendered to the dissolution in 1540, the abbot Thomas Clarke granted a sixty one year lease of property to Thomas Birkenhead. This lease was published in the *Cheshire Sheaf* in July 1937, and included "one Wyndemylne called Ireby Mylne". The indenture included the conditions that St. Werburgh's was responsible for "all necessary reparacons...that is to say mylne-stones, tymber werke and tymber for the same ironwerke and iron for the same, cogges...seyll clothes". One year's rent was 40s. payable "at the Feasts of St. Martin in Winter and the Nativity of St. John Baptist, by even portions".

After the dissolution the mill passed into the ownership of Chester Cathedral, which was granted the township of Irby in 1541. The windmill is referred to in ecclesiastical documents of the 16th and 17th centuries. For example, an indenture of 1552 printed in the *Cheshire Sheaf* in April 1902 mentioned "tythes belongith to ye said Cathedrell Church. Also one wynd-mill in Irby aforesayd cald Irby Mill". A lease of 1552 granted the mill from Chester Cathedral to Rowland Stanley. This was printed in the *Cheshire Sheaf* in October 1906 and stated that "the said Dean and Chapter have also demised to the said Roland Stanley...their Windy Milne called Irby Milne". Chester Cathedral still owned the mill in 1660, when they granted it to William Stanley. By 1684 the mill had passed into other hands for it is mentioned in the will of Edward Glegg of Grange in that year. Beazley's transcript of the will was printed in 'Wirral Records of the 17th Century' and includes the passage, "my will is that all my purchased lands in and about Irby with the wind mill there (shall be) sold by my executors; and if they do not agree...my sonne John shall sell the said lands and mill".

Another mill was built during the 18th century following the demise of the mill at the first site. It was probably constructed during the first twenty five years of the 1700s. In the *Journal of Merseyside Archaeological Society* an interesting point is raised. Although the second mill was always referred to as "Irby mill", like its predecessor, it actually stood just outside the boundaries of Irby, in Greasby township. The journal points out in 'Irby Mill Excavations 1979' that in the Thurstaston parish registers, under the date 1725, William Harrison the miller of "Irby mill-hill", was said to be in the "township of Greasby". This suggests that the mill had changed site by this date. Earlier parish register entries such as that of 1709, when the miller was James Morecroft, do not mention that the location was in Greasby township. Therefore it is possible that the change of site occurred between 1709 and 1725. This second windmill was one of the last post mills to work on Wirral and was a later post mill of the turret form. The earlier mill, which likely underwent various rebuildings, was doubtless a post mill of somewhat primitive construction, probably of simplistic tripod type.

The later post mill is shown on Burdett's map of 1777 and on Greenwood's map of 1819. Fearon and Eyes's coastal chart published in 1738 marks it as "Erby Mill". Accompanying the mill was a small sandstone miller's cottage. This was probably built in the early 19th century, sometime after the mill itself. Merseyside Archaeological Society dated the building to the 1830s. The cottage was once home to the Hales; this milling family ran the mill in the early 19th century. Richard Hale's will, proved in 1807, gives his occupation as a miller and records that he was a resident of Greasby. It has been postulated that his predecessor, another Richard Hale, along with his wife Anne, may have built the second mill. Their initials along with the date 1694 were formerly to be seen on a farmhouse situated on Irby Hill. The mill cottage, along with the windmill, was marked on the tithe map of c.1849, the plot they occupied being described as "House, Garden and Windmill". The tithe apportionment shows that the miller at this time was Edward Realey, who is also listed as a miller at Greasby in the *Post Office Directory of Cheshire* for 1857. Later on the mill was worked by Charles Fernyhough, who is said to have been the last miller. He is listed as a "farmer & miller" at Irby in the *Post Office Directory of Cheshire* for 1878. It may actually have been William Atkinson who was the last to work Irby mill, for he is listed in *Slater's Directory* of 1883, towards the end of the mill's working life.

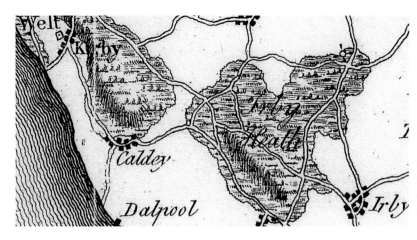

43. Burdett marked the site of the later Irby post mill with a cross symbol, at the northern edge of "Irby Heath".

The second mill stopped working in the latter half of the 1880s and stood unused for nearly a decade. It became increasingly ruinous, with large pieces blown off during high winds. One of the sails blew off during the 1890s and some years later in 1898, the mill had become so dilapidated that the decision was made to pull it down. This was mainly due to the threat which it posed to the nearby miller's cottage. The cottage was still inhabited by the former miller and the mill was getting increasingly dangerous. Mitford Abraham said that the miller "was much afraid of it being blown down upon his house". Colonel Arthur Mesham owned the mill and cottage at this date and writing in *Notes and Queries* in 1899 he stated "the old mill was in a ruinous condition and dangerous, and I had to pull it down". Colonel Arthur Mesham had bought the mill from John Ralph Shaw whose ownership went back to the mid-19th century. In the same journal Mesham refers to rollers in his possession made of bone, an inch in diameter and five to six inches long. It appears that these rollers may have been fitted around the top wall of the roundhouse, so as to ease rotation of the body of the mill.

44. This Ordnance Survey map from the late 1890s describes Irby mill as "In Ruins". (Courtesy of and Copyright Old-Maps and Ordnance Survey)

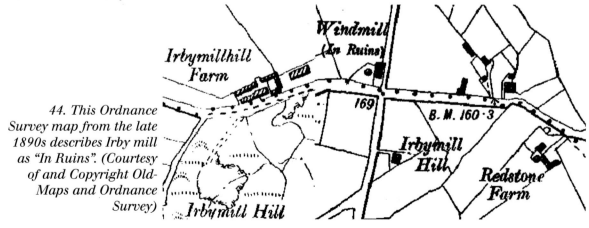

When it was pulled down in 1898, the mill nearly severely injured those who demolished it. They were not trained in such matters and began the job by pulling blocks out of the roundhouse, without propping up the body of the mill which it supported. The woodwork began to creak and groan providing just enough warning for the men to escape as the mill crashed to the ground. It is a real shame that this post mill has disappeared, but one can understand the danger it must have posed to those living nearby. Mitford Abraham said of its destruction "in a second or two this once picturesque little landmark was in a ruined mass on the ground".

When Mitford Abraham visited the site in 1903 he described a "confused heap of ruins" at the site of the mill. Various woodwork remained and some of the pieces of timber such as the main shaft were several feet square, apparently "many a miller had scratched his initials and date on the shaft of his mill". Unfortunately Mitford Abraham only seems to have recorded the oldest date visible – "the shaft, bears the date 1773 and the initials RMH [Richard M. Hale]"; he hypothesised that "You cannot infer from this that the mill was then built...However it is just possible that this is the date of destruction of the older mill and alteration of site". As previously mentioned, this seems rather late; more evidence points to this mill being built in the first quarter of the 18th century.

45. This is the earliest known photograph of Irby mill and likely dates from the 1880s. It must have been taken whilst the mill was still in use, for the sailcloths are in place, ready to be unfurled. (Courtesy of Birkenhead Reference Library)

46. This watercolour by Harold Hopps is dated 1897 and shows Irby mill with four sails. The mill would have been disused for a decade at this point and Hopps probably improved the appearance of the disused building, for the mill may even have been missing a sail when painted. (Courtesy of the Williamson Art Gallery and Museum)

47. By the later 1890s Irby mill was in a ruinous state, with three sails remaining. This photograph dates to around the time that the mill was demolished in 1898. (Courtesy of Birkenhead Reference Library)

48. This view showing the rear of Irby post mill dates from 1898, the same year that the mill was demolished. The miller's cottage may be seen in the background. (Courtesy of Ian Boumphrey)

49. Photographs of Irby mill from the late 1890s reveal the body of the mill to have been covered in several layers of weatherboarding, which later started to become detached. (Courtesy of Ian Boumphrey)

50. The tailpole of Irby mill was equipped with a spoked wheel, which would have facilitated rotation of the structure. By 1898 this wheel had largely fallen to pieces. (Courtesy of Ian Boumphrey)

51. The site of Irby mill c.1901. The demolition of the mill was evidently
thorough and little evidence, even of the roundhouse, can be seen.
A few timbers remain behind the men. (Courtesy of Ian Boumphrey)

The miller's cottage remains to this day. After the miller left, it changed hands several times. George and Bertha Lumsden bought the cottage in 1919 and in 1924 they opened the building as "The Old Mill Café". In 1938 Higson's Brewery bought the building from the Lumsdens and rented it out. They wanted to open a pub but planning permission was rejected on multiple occasions. The brewery continued to apply for planning permission for some forty years until they eventually gained permission in the 1970s. Planning permission was granted on the condition that the original mill cottage was retained and any extensions had to be in keeping with the original building. The building has several extensions; one runs parallel to the original dwelling and another is perpendicular. The core of the building is still formed by the original mill cottage. Conversion to a pub began in 1978 and by 1980 the extended cottage had been opened as a pub called "The Mill", it is now called the "Irby Mill". As the cottage was converted it was noted that at some point the building appeared to have formed two separate dwellings.

52. The Old Mill Café
is seen in the former
miller's cottage of Irby
mill in 1924. (Courtesy
of Ian Boumphrey)

During the conversion Merseyside Archaeological Society carried out excavations at the site. Their records state that, "landscaping of the area west and north of the cottage to provide space for parking…would destroy any evidence which remained of the mill site." The society recorded a "flat topped mound" on the site of the mill. A trench was excavated here and much pottery was unearthed. No definitive evidence of the mill itself was found and it was concluded in their report that – "The late material found in almost all the levels and the lack of features seemed to indicate that all archaeological traces of the mill must have been removed when the area was levelled after its demolition." Some reused "sandstone and brick of 18th century date" were found in the vicinity and these could well have come from the mill. Later, the whole mound was reduced to the surrounding level by machine. As a result of this operation "a fragment of mill stone was uncovered on the north side of the mound which was retained by the contractors for display outside the building". The archaeological report includes no other information on this millstone fragment. The fragment is certainly not outside the pub anymore and unfortunately I have been unable to trace it, although it is still remembered by local people.

Within the pub, few original features can be seen, although there are a few points where the rough sandstone walls of the old cottage are visible through the plaster. The chimney of one of the original fireplaces is also present. The site of the post mill betrays nothing of its past today. The entire area has been extensively landscaped and although it is possible to work out, to some accuracy, the site on which the mill stood, there is nothing there to see. Alongside the pub which bears its name, the road names Mill Hill Road and Mill Lane are the main reminders of this mill.

53. The Irby Mill pub in 2014. The original mill cottage lies between the two chimneys, the left-hand end of the building being a 1970s extension. The mill itself stood behind and to the left of the cottage.

4.3 Thingwall Mill

The first known record of a windmill in Thingwall is in papers relating to the Poole family; a letter dating to 1650 records that the annual rent was £5 in that year. The Pooles leased the windmill in a 1722 lease which was published in the *Cheshire Sheaf* in July 1939 and reads – "Francis Poole of Poole esquire, son and heir apparent of Sir James Poole of Poole, baronet; grants to Henry Wolstenholme of Neston, yeoman and James Wade of Upton, yeoman a piece of land in Thingwall, whereupon a windmill called Thingwall Mill now or late stood...". The wording of this lease is peculiar, for it seems to be a lease for the land on Thingwall Hill rather than for the mill itself.

The age of the initial structure is uncertain. According to Mitford Abraham it had no stage. From this comment we can gather that he believed it was an early tower mill. Williams and Crompton also suggested that the mill was a simple tower mill of three storey pattern. However, on Wirral the 1720s would make for an early tower mill indeed and given a mill also existed here in the mid-17th century, it seems probable that the mill was in fact a post mill. Alternatively two windmills, both a post mill and an early tower mill could have stood here in the period 1650-1866, before the last mill was built. This possibility is, to some extent, corroborated by a photographic copy of an undated painting in Mitford Abraham's collection at the Mills Archive. The painting is of a small tower mill, purportedly the early mill at Thingwall. The whereabouts of the original painting is not certain, and it is unknown whether it genuinely shows Thingwall mill. Intriguingly the mill in the painting appears to have a cap rotated by a long tailpole. The earlier mill is shown on Burdett's map of 1777, Greenwood's map of 1819 and Bryant's map of 1831. It is also marked on Fearon and Eyes's coastal chart of 1738, Williamson's chart of 1766 and Burdett's chart of 1771.

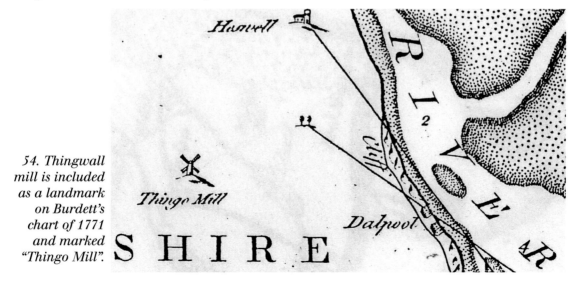

54. Thingwall mill is included as a landmark on Burdett's chart of 1771 and marked "Thingo Mill".

The original windmill was replaced by a new, brick built tower mill in 1866; this bore a datestone with the legend "re-erected by Robert Capper, 1866". The mill was four storeys in height, with a stage at the level of the first floor. This was the last windmill to be built on Wirral, yet it was of a simple design. Equipped with a chain wheel and common sails it was somewhat reminiscent of a previous era, even when newly built. The Cappers were a milling family who worked this mill and its predecessor for well over a century. The Capper family became the millers here sometime during the 18th century. They have left a number of 19th century wills in the Cheshire Record Office, which record them as millers by occupation. According to Greg Dawson writing in *Arwe* – "the Hall family ran the windmill during the 1720s, followed by the Oliverson family in the 1730s. After James Oliverson left Thingwall, the Capper family from Nantwich took over the windmill".

A sequence of events led to the demise of this mill, the first being when one of the sails was blown down during a storm on 1st January 1897. Soon after the storm, the last miller pper died of tongue cancer, whilst aged in his fifties. The mill never worked r these events. Ann Capper, Robert's wife, died three years later in 1900 and the lemolished in the same year. Mitford Abraham wrote that it was – "bought for)cal farmer, who resold it to a Liverpool timber merchant for twice the sum, and 1 demolished".

gwall mill was shown to be working as a flour mill on this Ordnance Survey map of c.1875. (Courtesy of and Copyright Old-Maps and Ordnance Survey)

once a small collection of dwellings clustered around the mill, which stood d. They formed a small settlement, entirely separate from the main village and are shown on the tithe map of c.1849. Most of these buildings, like the windmill, were owned by the Capper family, originally by Samuel Capper and later by his son Robert. The first of the Cappers' old buildings is Baker's Cottage; this is the most southerly old cottage on the east side of Mill Road. Just north of this building is a row of three terraced houses built c.1880; Greg Dawson refers to these as "Mill Cottages". The next cottage along is Mill Cottage which is dated 1797. It may once have housed the miller and predates the tower mill of 1866. Just after Mill Cottage there is a trackway which leads along to the fourth of the Cappers' properties, Lavender Cottage (previously Mill Yard). Leaving the trackway and returning to Mill Road there is one last building, just north of the trackway, which also belonged to the Cappers. Originally called Mill House it was the home of the Capper family. Later on, probably in the 1850s, it was converted to a public house called the Mill Inn, which finally closed in 1914. *The Post Office Directory of Cheshire* for 1857 lists Samuel Capper as a "miller and beer retailer", suggesting the Cappers' inn was open by that point.

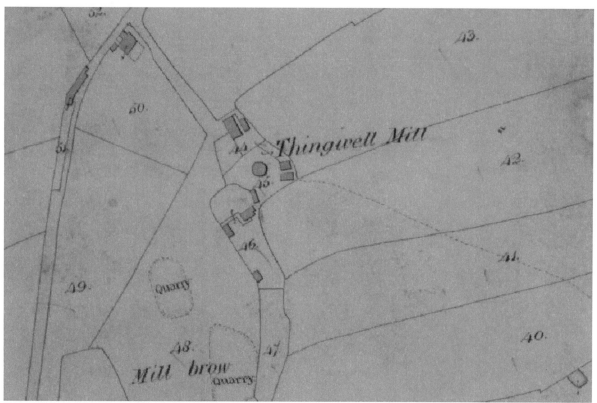

56. The tithe map shows the cluster of buildings around Thingwall mill, all of which belonged to the Capper family. (Courtesy of Cheshire Archives and Local Studies)

57. An early photograph showing Thingwall mill whilst it was still at work, this view probably dates to the late 1880s. A figure seen upon the stage could be the miller. The building to the right is Lavender Cottage. (Courtesy of Ian Boumphrey)

58. Thingwall mill with a missing sail, presumably that which was blown down on New Year's Day 1897, forcing the mill out of use. The photograph probably dates from 1897 and the condition of the mill evidently deteriorated rapidly after it ceased to work. (Courtesy of Greg Dawson)

59. Harold Hopps produced this painting of Thingwall mill in 1906, some years after its demolition. However, the mill was a building Hopps knew whilst it was still at work, for he produced another painting of it in 1892. (Courtesy of the Williamson Art Gallery and Museum)

60. Thingwall mill had only two sails remaining and was missing a large portion of its stage in this photograph c.1898. The building to the far left of the picture was the Mill Inn. (Courtesy of the Mills Archive Trust)

61. Thingwall mill was sold to a Liverpool timber merchant in 1900, prior to its demolition in the same year. It seems likely that this photograph dates to 1900, and it may be no coincidence that many wooden fittings appear to have been removed for reuse. (Courtesy of Ian Boumphrey)

The windmill itself stood directly west of Lavender Cottage, on a plot of land which bordered Mill Road. The last relic of Thingwall mill is some millstones built into the wall of the trackway that leads to Lavender Cottage. Two millstone halves are visible and unless a significant amount of each millstone extends below the ground it may well be that this is a single stone split in two. Mitford Abraham wrote of a wall "into which several bits of millstones are built, as well as two date stones, one bearing 'Robert Capper, Thingwell Mill, 1880', which came from the old kiln, and the other 're-erected by Robert Capper, 1866', the date of the erection of the last mill". This kiln was probably used to dry oats prior to grinding, for Thingwall mill was notable for its oatmeal production. Unfortunately I have been unable to locate these datestones, despite the millstones still being clearly visible. The millstones are made from a coarse gritstone, possibly originating from Derbyshire. They are somewhat weathered, forming part of the lowest visible course of the wall which once surrounded the final windmill. It is quite possible that these millstones predate the final mill and that they were used in an earlier mill.

The site of the mill is now occupied by a modern bungalow. This has been built behind the wall containing the millstones and covers the site of the mill. This house was built in relatively recent years. In June 1997, when the initial preparations for the construction of the house were being made, the foundations of Thingwall mill were uncovered on the building site. According to the late local historian Jim O'Neil various large sandstone blocks were exposed as the land was excavated. The mill was brick built but the foundations must have included local sandstone. Mitford Abraham wrote – "The foundations of the mill were not on rock but on sand, into which the base was built for nearly 6 feet." He also wrote in 1903 that – "The site of the mill and the ground around has now been levelled". If the foundations penetrated as deeply as six feet it is easy to see how some were left behind. The site could doubtless have been levelled whilst leaving some of the mill's foundations intact.

62. The old mill yard which lay in front of Thingwall mill in 2014; the bungalow to the right of the wall occupies the site of the mill itself.

63. Two sections of gritstone millstone at Thingwall. These are built into the wall which once surrounded the 1866 tower mill.

64. Mill Cottage in 2009; it has a datestone of 1797 and was once one of the Cappers' properties.

65. Mill House which was the Capper family home, before being converted to the Mill Inn.

4.4 Gayton Mill

The windmill at Gayton, in the parish of Heswall, is an early example of a tower mill on Wirral. The oldest tower mill remaining on Wirral, it was reputedly the first mill of this type ever to be built on the peninsula. The mill probably dates from the 1730s. However, it could be somewhat older and is sometimes said to date from the late 17th century, such as by Randall in *The Search for Old Wirral*. The mill bears a datestone of somewhat unofficial nature, merely a date carved into one of the sandstone blocks, beneath a window. It purportedly reads "1735" although it is rather weathered; the initials "EL" are carved into the same block. This date suggests that the building certainly existed around that time and it could well denote the approximate date of construction. An earlier reference to a windmill at Heswall is recorded in a plea roll dated 1357, a translation of which has been published as *Cheshire Forest Eyre Roll 1357*. This document mentions that a windmill, "*molendinum ventriticum*", was built in Heswall c.1327 and this mill still existed in 1357. This would have been a medieval post mill, and given it was said to stand in Heswall township, rather than Gayton township, it is unlikely to have occupied the same site as Gayton mill. It may even have ceased to work some centuries before Gayton mill was built.

A mill is marked at Gayton on Fearon and Eyes's coastal chart of 1738, showing that Gayton mill did indeed exist from at least the 1730s, as their survey was conducted in 1736 and 1737. The mill is next shown on Williamson's Chart of *Liverpool and Parkgate Harbours* published in 1766. It is marked on Burdett's harbour chart of 1771 as "Gayton Mill" and also on his Cheshire map of 1777. It was missed off Greenwood's map of 1819, but it is shown on the revision of Greenwood's map published in 1830. Gayton mill was formerly part of the Glegg estate, indeed it could well have been the Glegg family who were responsible for its construction. Many of the Glegg family estate papers, some dating back to the 17th century, are preserved at Cheshire Record Office. It could be that these documents would substantiate an early connection between this mill and the Gleggs. During the mid-19th century the mill was owned by John Baskervyle Glegg of Gayton, who had earlier been the Sheriff of Cheshire. The miller at this point was Samuel Woodward, as recorded on the tithe apportionment of c.1851. James Worrall was working the mill in 1864. He was recorded as a "farmer and miller" in *Morris & Co.'s Directory of Cheshire* of that year.

The tower of this mill is unusually squat and is constructed from blocks of the local red sandstone. It stands some twenty five feet tall and has three floors. Despite being such a small tower mill, during its working life there were three pairs of stones, which were observed by Mitford Abraham after closure. The wooden windshaft was slotted to take the sails; one of the two pairs was positioned in front of the other. This mill was an early casualty, and stopped working during the later 1870s. James Woodward, presumably related to the Samuel Woodward listed on the tithe apportionment, was recorded as a miller and farmer on the census of 1871. However, on the 1881 census he was simply listed as a farmer, showing that the mill had ceased to work by the 1880s. The last miller at Gayton apparently raised a family of sixteen children! Despite the mill being disused for some decades by 1903, Mitford Abraham said "the works are absolutely complete". The condition of the mill deteriorated once out of use and by the late 19th century no sails remained. The windmill historian Rex Wailes, writing in his classic *The English Windmill*, described how transmission from the great spur wheel to the millstones in windmills, was archaically transmitted via lantern pinions, as opposed to simple spur gears. In 1954 he said that most examples of lantern pinions had disappeared, but that he had observed an example at Gayton mill, demonstrating that the milling machinery here was of considerable age.

66. Fearon and Eyes's Chart of 1737 marks Gayton tower mill. The windmill is drawn below the word "Gayton".

67. Gayton mill was recorded as milling both corn and flour on the Ordnance Survey map of c.1875. (Courtesy of and Copyright Old-Maps and Ordnance Survey)

Lionel Roberts sent his memories of the mill to *The Wirral Journal* in the 1980s. He recalled the condition of the mill in the first decades of the 20th century – "Each autumn about the years 1915-16, my father purchased from Mr Lightfoot, the owner of the mill, apples and pears from the orchard surrounding the mill…During the day I would take the opportunity to explore the mill, climb the stairs and marvel at the huge millstones, and how human beings were able to raise them to such a height…there were pieces of sailcloth strewn about the place". At this point the mill's interior remained in reasonable condition, for nothing had changed since the last day the mill was worked.

In the 1920s the derelict mill was included in the property of a neighbouring house owned by the Lewis family. Even in the later years of the 1920s, the milling machinery on all three floors remained intact. The owners of the house used the ground floor as a coal store and would collect coal several times each day. One morning it was discovered that all three floors and the machinery had fallen to the base of the tower. After around half a century disused, the floors had rotted severely and they gave way suddenly during the night. The owners of the house had previously enquired about the possibility of saving the building. They were told that restoration could not be achieved, because the very fabric of the mill was in such poor condition. The sandstone blocks forming the tower were badly weathered and beginning to crack.

68. Gayton mill had already been out of use for over fifteen years when this photograph was taken in the mid-1890s. At this date the heavily constructed wheel for an endless chain remained in place. (Courtesy of Ian Boumphrey)

69. This view of Gayton mill was taken by Mitford Abraham around the turn of the 20th century. Standing to the right of the disused mill is the former Mill Cottage, which exists to this day. (Courtesy of The Heswall Society)

70. In c.1905 the chain wheel at Gayton mill was in a fragmentary condition and there were many holes in the cap. (Courtesy of Ian Boumphrey)

71. In the opening years of the 20th century Gayton mill appears to have been in occasional use for storage purposes. (Courtesy of Ian Boumphrey)

72. This photograph shows Gayton mill in a somewhat dilapidated and derelict state around the turn of the 20th century. (Courtesy of the Mills Archive Trust)

73. In the early 20th century the cap and windshaft at Gayton mill remained in reasonable condition, especially considering the mill had ceased to work some decades earlier. (Courtesy of the Mills Archive Trust)

74. In 1936 the derelict tower of Gayton mill stood within the garden of the neighbouring house, seen to the left of this photograph. (Courtesy of Special Collections and Archives, Templeman Library, University of Kent)

The building is grade two listed and an inspection was made when it was first listed in 1962. At this point the derelict interior was said to contain the "fallen remains of timber structure". By the 1960s the cap was missing, but it had remained in good preservation right into the later 1930s. Williams and Crompton reported that the wooden windshaft remained in place until it collapsed in 1963. Other sources suggest that the windshaft and parts of the cap did not finally collapse until 1969. Writing in 1976 Williams and Crompton noted that – "Some of the wooden cleats to which the luffing rope could be attached are still present"; a remarkable survivor after a century of disuse. Writing for the North West Mills Group in 1983 Roberts remarked that – "The mill today is in a very sad state. The red sandstone tower is crumbling very badly, although still standing to full height, with the iron curb ring with the toothed rack on top…the machinery that remains is in a tangled heap on the ground floor. The machinery is all of wood. Many items of interest can be picked out from the rubble. One pair of large one-piece stones remain in situ on a hurst and parts of French burrs are lying outside the mill".

Several parties inspected the mill with restoration in mind over the years. In the end they all agreed that the building was a lost cause. According to the late local historian Jim O'Neil much of the mill's machinery remained within the tower right up until 1989. At this time a rescue operation was mounted and some machinery was recovered from the tower. Despite the passage of over a century since the mill stopped working, some of the parts were mechanically sound. Exact details are scarce; it has been said that some parts were used in the restoration of other historic windmills. Unfortunately I have been unable to find any record of exactly what was recovered from the mill.

75. Remarkably, in the late 1950s the framework of the cap still survived at Gayton mill, despite the mill having been disused for around eighty years. The windshaft fell into the tower during the 1960s. (Courtesy of the Mills Archive Trust)

76. Detail of the doorway into Gayton mill in 1983. Many of the sandstone blocks forming the tower were obviously in a poor condition at this point. (Courtesy of Jim O'Neil)

*77. The ivy covered tower of Gayton mill as
it appeared in 1983. By the 1970s the cap
and windshaft had both entirely collapsed
(Courtesy of Jim O'Neil)*

Planning permission was granted to incorporate the mill into a modern housing
development in June 1989. The permission was granted to PJ Allison Ltd. who had bought
the land on which the mill stood. This led to the mill being restored and saved the building
from a sad fate. If it had continued to decay for much longer the tower would undoubtedly
have fallen down. To save the original structure a breezeblock wall was constructed
inside the tower, this supports the original sandstone blocks. Concrete rings were used
as additional support at the new floor levels. The restored mill has three floors and one of
these is under a replacement cap. Two other floors are within the sandstone tower. Since
this is a relatively small mill it was not large enough to form a self-contained home. A new
building which adjoins the tower had to be constructed.

Various pieces of wood which remained within the tower were incorporated into the new
house. These include the main post which would have rotated within the mill's upper
storey. This old windmill is still an obvious feature to the traveller on Telegraph Road and
the house of which it is a component stands in Gayton Mill Close, which comes off Mill
Lane. A number of millstones may be seen in the grounds of the house, but it is not known

if they originate from Gayton mill, or if they were acquired from elsewhere to display in the gardens of the property. Alongside the mill there is a house named "The Old Granary" which appears to be formed from two adjoining buildings. One of these is probably the granary and the second another former storage building, both with alterations and extensions. Just east of this house is another residence standing in a road called Old Mill Close. This house is called "Old Mill Cottage" and must once have been the miller's home. All of these extant buildings are shown on the tithe map of c.1851.

78. The house conversion which includes Gayton mill, as seen in 2007.

79. Gayton mill, as seen from the garden of the house of which it is now a component. (Courtesy of Ian Hughes)

4.5 Neston Mills

In the early years of the 18th century, a single windmill stood in the Leighton area of Great Neston. This mill was part of the Mostyn estate and is shown on an estate map of 1732. The mill stood on Leighton Road, just north of the junction with Wood Lane. The 1732 field book of Neston, which accompanies the map in the Mostyn manuscripts, refers to this mill as the "new windmill"; this was reported by Geoffrey Place in the *Cheshire Sheaf* in November 1977. Sir Roger Mostyn is recorded to have had a mill built at Neston in 1729; he paid £180, employing the millwright Laurence Tyror. This is presumably the new mill marked on the Mostyn estate map.

The date of construction is somewhat early for a tower mill and would rival Gayton's claim as Wirral's earliest such mill; a late post mill certainly seems more likely. *Neston: Stone Age to Steam Age* mentions bricks being fired on Neston Heath to repair the mill. Given the period this seems to suggest a turret post mill with a substantial brick roundhouse, although one cannot be certain that this mill was not an early tower mill. In 1731 the new mill was leased to John Broadhurst at £12 for the year. He was evidently not the ideal tenant, for according to *Neston: Stone Age to Steam Age*, the Mostyn manuscripts record that he "brake the mill, run away with the people's corn and bags, paid no rent". By 1732 the rent had more than doubled to £25 per annum. This rent was payable to the Mostyns by John Evans, who employed two other millers at the mill alongside himself.

The 1732 estate map also records another windmill in a different area of the township, at a position on the southern side of what is now Raby Park Road. This mill is listed as the "old windmill in the road without any land" and it evidently occupied the older site in the township. A mill existed in this area from at least 1596 at which date, according to Place, "Neston Myll" was leased to George Ledsham by the Earl of Derby. It seems quite plausible that this mention is a reference to the Raby Park Road site. Another likely reference to this mill is in *Neston: Stone Age to Steam Age*, which mentions a document cataloguing items associated with a mill in Neston in 1610. The list included the mill's sailcloths which were described as "two of them reasonable good cloths and the other two something worse".

This mill would have been a post mill and in 1610 the annual rent paid to the Mostyn family was £6 13s. 4d. The millers at this time were Robert Holme and Roger Higginson; in 1639 there was a new miller named William Evans. The mill was still operating in 1733, when it is listed as having been repaired. However, it is not indicated on the Mostyn estate map of 1811 and certainly seems to have disappeared by that point, nor was it included on Burdett's survey, so it was probably disused by 1772-1774. The Great Neston tithe map of 1847 shows a large group of twelve adjoining fields to the north of Raby Park Road.

These have names such as "Big Mill Hay", "Old Mill Brow", "Mill Hill" etc., and are taken to derive their names from this windmill, the approximate site of which they must denote.

Sometime later in the 18th century a second windmill was built, just north of the 1729 mill on Leighton Road. Both these mills are shown on Burdett's map published in 1777, and so the later one must have been built in the years between 1732 and Burdett surveying Cheshire (1772-1774). This second mill was also under the ownership of the Mostyn family. It was a three storey, brick built tower mill and for many years it and the older mill existed simultaneously. There are many instances of an older mill being replaced by an entirely new structure nearby. However, for two windmills to be constructed within the space of forty years and then worked side by side is unusual in this area. In 1793 one of the millers at Neston mills, James Bullen, was killed having been struck by one of the sails.

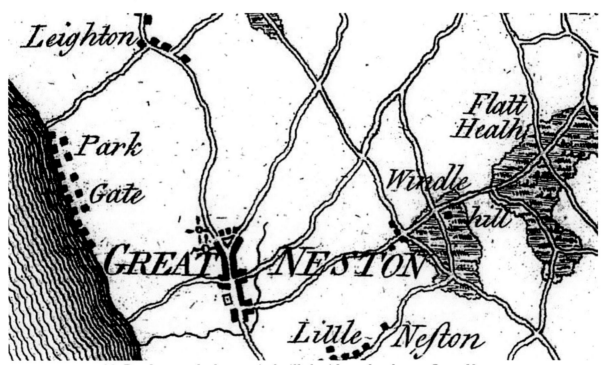

80. Burdett marked two windmills beside each other at Great Neston.

An estate map of 1814 and Bryant's map of 1831 also show both mills. Only a single mill is shown on Greenwood's map of 1819; however, this was evidently a mistake for the revised edition of 1830 marks both mills. The fact that the older mill survived in unison with the newer mill for so long indicates that they must have worked simultaneously. This is confirmed by an advertisement in the *Chester Courant* of 13th November 1810 which publicises the auction of – "two cornmills in Neston in complete repair…In each of the mills there is one pair of Greys [millstones], one dressing machine, and a dressing mill with fan and screen for cleaning wheat". A house, cowhouse and stable adjoining the mills were included in the same sale. Another advertisement was placed in the *Chester Chronicle* of 6th December 1822, on behalf of Sir Thomas Mostyn, and also refers to both mills. In this period Sir Thomas Mostyn's tenants occupying land in Neston, Parkgate, Thornton Hough and Leighton were obliged to grind their grain at Neston mills, an arrangement enforced in the tenants' leases.

The earlier mill of 1729 does not appear on maps after the early 1830s and is not shown on the first edition Ordnance Survey map of c.1840. It is said that this mill was destroyed by a great storm. Place, writing in the *Cheshire Sheaf* in November 1977, related that the *Chester Chronicle* recorded severe storm damage to both mills on 13th December 1822. Indeed, this newspaper reports that the top of the older mill was "quite blown off". He postulated that the earlier mill may have gone out of use at this point, having already been disused for some years when indicated on Bryant's 1831 survey. This seems to be a satisfactory and likely explanation as to when this mill stopped working. All evidence of the 1729 mill has now long since disappeared.

The later mill continued to work long after the disappearance of the 1729 mill. It was marked on the tithe map of 1847. At this point the owner was Edward Mostyn Lloyd Mostyn. He was the 2nd Baron Mostyn, died in 1884, and was once a Member of Parliament for Flintshire. The mill's occupier in the mid-19th century was Thomas Lee, who must have been the miller. A cottage was included within the same plot on the tithe map and this once stood in-between the two mills. A decade later Neston mill was being worked by the Hale family of Wirral millers. Richard Hale was recorded here in the *Post Office Directory of Cheshire* dated 1857. There was then a further change in the family working the mill, for *Morris & Co.'s Directory of Cheshire* gives James Radley as the miller here in 1864. The mill was still in the hands of the Radley family in 1878, for the *Post Office Directory of Cheshire* for that year, lists a Mrs. Eliza Radley as both a corn miller and a shop keeper in Great Neston.

The mill is marked as producing flour on the Ordnance Survey map of c.1875. It continued to work up until around 1885. Certainly it was still working in 1883, for Robert Bridson was recorded there in *Slater's Directory* of that year. He may well have been the last miller. During the last years of its working life the mill operated with only two sails. Mitford Abraham claimed that – "Owing to its proximity to the roadway the arms [sails], when revolving on a sunny day, reflected on the road. It was a peculiar sight, and many a horse would refuse to go by till the mill was stopped".

81. Only one windmill existed at Neston at the time of this Ordnance Survey map c.1910 and even that was out of use. (Courtesy of and Copyright Old-Maps and Ordnance Survey)

The mill was gutted soon after closure, with all of the machinery removed. A writer in the *Cheshire Sheaf* in December 1898 described the mill as "begrimed, dismantled, and woefully forlorn. It stands a complete wreck of its former usefulness". Mitford Abraham said in reference to the mill's closure – "all the works were removed shortly afterwards, and the building is now used as a joiner's shop". This may refer to the business which the Gray family operated around the turn of the 20th century, when they occupied the mill yard. The mill seems to have spent much of the 20th century in a semi-derelict state, as shown by many old photographs.

82. This photograph shows Neston mill, probably at the end of the 1890s, around fifteen years after it had ceased to work. By this point it had already lost its cap, which had been replaced by a conical roof. (Courtesy of the Mills Archive Trust)

83. Neston mill standing in Leighton Road around 1911. One of the windows appears to be missing from the tower. (Courtesy of Ian Boumphrey)

84. This rural scene c.1910 shows the junction of Parkgate Road and Earle Drive. The tower of Neston mill may be seen in the background, across the fields. (Courtesy of Ian Boumphrey)

85. Neston mill appears to be in a slightly neglected condition in this photograph of 1914. The miller's cottage stands behind the mill, a little further along Leighton Road. (Courtesy of Ian Boumphrey)

86. Neston mill in the 1930s; at this time the Gray family carried out a range of activities in the mill yard alongside the mill, including wheelwrighting and blacksmithing. (Courtesy of Ian Boumphrey)

The building is now grade two listed. The listing information of 1962 confirms that "all mill fixtures and fittings have been removed". In 1962 the *Liverpool Daily Post* stated that Neston mill had been restored and that it was being used as a garage at that time. The mill was further renovated in 1975 by Robert Ellison and Lesley Blackburne. It was from here that they ran their glass engraving business. The mill continued serving this function until 1990 on Robert Ellison's retirement. Afterwards the mill became a house and still proudly serves that function today. The mill has a replacement cap which was installed at some point after 1980; in that year the mill had a flat roof. Since the 1950s, W. Bibby Ltd. has operated their engineering business from the mill yard alongside the property.

The fabric of the mill's tower appears to have been extensively altered during the past. Additional doorways seem to have been inserted and a garage has been attached on to the Leighton Road frontage. One doorway has been added at the front, leading to a level above this garage. There is also a doorway on the opposite side at ground level; it is unclear if this is one of the mill's original entrances, or yet another addition. In two places there are rows of large windows down the side of the mill. These windows do not all appear on old photographs and some of them are certainly modern additions. The original tower was fairly windowless and more natural light was presumably a requirement, for converting it to a useable building. The original windows can be identified by the style of the brickwork around them. There is a house called "Mill Cottage", which still stands just past the mill in Leighton Road. This was marked on the tithe map and once lay directly between the two mills. It is almost certainly the former miller's residence.

87. Neston mill as seen from Leighton Road in 2009.

88. By 1980 Neston mill was restored and in commercial use. The mill had a flat roof at this time. (Courtesy of the Mills Archive Trust)

89. Some of the windows at Neston mill appear to have been inserted when it was converted for alternative use.

90. A view of the converted tower mill at Neston in 2008.

CHAPTER 5: MILLS OF WIRRAL'S MERSEY SIDE

5.1 Tranmere Mill

A brick built tower mill used to stand on the high ground of Holt Hill in Tranmere, near to the point where Mill Close (formerly Mill Street) joins Church Road. Given this mill existed into relatively recent times, very little has been written about it and few details are given in the main historical accounts of Tranmere. The mill was once owned by the Lightbounds, a Wirral milling family who also owned Higher Bebington and Willaston mills.

There are purportedly records which indicate the presence of a medieval mill in Tranmere township. If a post mill did exist here, then it seemingly ceased to exist many years before the construction of the tower mill in the same township. On the basis of field names an earlier mill may have been located to the south of the later mill. The tithe map of 1843 marks two fields to the south, both called "Mill Hill". However, according to Dodgson, J. E. Allison could find no evidence of a mill at this site.

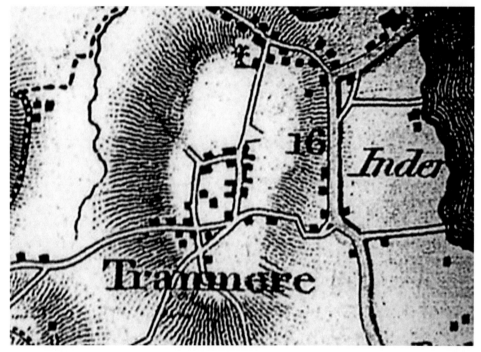

91. Greenwood's map is the first known to mark a windmill in Tranmere township.

Mitford Abraham said that this mill was "built about the same time as the present Bebington Mill". From this it can be concluded that the mill was likely built around the turn of the 19th century. Greenwood's survey of Cheshire of 1819 is the earliest map on which Tranmere mill is marked and it is also marked on Bryant's map of 1831. Perhaps the best indication of this mill's age comes from the will of Samuel Lightbound, who was the owner of Storeton mill until his death in 1798. According to Alsbury, writing in *Fir-Bob Land*, Samuel had at least three sons to whom he left Tranmere, Willaston and Storeton mills. This seems to suggest that Tranmere mill was built in the late 18th century. It is not marked on Burdett's map of 1777 and does not seem to have existed in the period 1772-1774 when this was surveyed, so it was probably built between 1774 and 1798.

92. Bryant marked Tranmere mill on Holt Hill and labelled it as "The Mill".

What is particularly interesting is that in 1798 the mill was already in the ownership of the Lightbound family. Tranmere mill would have been fairly new at this point. It seems to provide an early example of a taller tower mill on Wirral and was probably not pre-1790s in origin, although the 1780s are possible. I think it likely that the Lightbounds were the family responsible for its construction. It would seem that this was the first mill to stand in Tranmere for some time; it had no direct predecessor. The construction of a tower mill was certainly something the Lightbounds were game to undertake. They formerly worked post mills at both Willaston and Storeton, but later built tower mills as replacements at both these sites. The mighty Willaston mill was built c.1800 by the Lightbound family, they also built Higher Bebington mill within the first few decades of the 19th century. The family must have had a lot of knowledge in this field, to have initiated the construction of these buildings. Based on their ownership of this mill, so early in its existence, it does seem a distinct possibility that the Lightbounds undertook the construction of this third, less appreciated mill.

Mitford Abraham had little to say on the subject of this mill, but did report that, "It was pulled down about thirty years ago" (in 1903). This suggests that the mill was demolished in the early 1870s, a date supported by the fact that the mill is not marked on the Ordnance Survey map of c.1875. At the date of demolition it could have been some time since the mill was last worked, but of its working history details are even more scant. Tranmere mill was presumably working in 1850; at this point Samuel Lightbound was listed as a corn miller in Tranmere in *Bagshaw's Cheshire Directory*. The mill is not listed in *Morris & Co.'s Directory of Cheshire* dated 1864. An earlier directory of Cheshire is the *Post Office Directory* dating to 1857. However, this does not list any millers at Tranmere either, despite doing so at other local sites. The lack of reference in the commercial sections of these local directories seems to suggest the mill had closed by the early 1860s, and may even have done so during the 1850s.

It is not known if any photographs were ever taken of Tranmere mill. However, two old paintings exist which show the building. These pictures are so similar that one must surely be based on the other; a photographic copy of the first is in Mitford Abraham's collection at the John Rylands Library; the other, signed W. F. Crook and dated 1841, is at the Williamson Art Gallery. These paintings show Tranmere mill to have been a tall tower mill of about five storeys. It was surrounded by a stage and the cap was rotated by a chain wheel. Cleats for affixing the endless chain may be seen above the stage. Various buildings adjoined the mill tower and these are shown on the tithe map of c.1843. The mill house which is shown on the tithe map can also be seen. If compared to Willaston and Higher Bebington mills, certain similarities in the design may be observed. In fact, the similarity to Willaston mill is striking. This seems strong further evidence that the Lightbounds built this mill, maybe employing the same millwright.

Intriguingly, a chimney stack and engine house may be seen to the right of the mill in the paintings. This seems to suggest that the windmill was fitted with a stationary steam engine by the early 1840s, based on the 1841 date on the Williamson Art Gallery's painting. One wonders why Tranmere mill stopped working so early, especially if it was facilitated by steam power? The death of a Samuel Lightbound described as a "baker and flour dealer" was registered in 1863. Samuel was aged fifty nine and a resident of Tranmere. He was not described as a miller, but must have had a connection to the mill. If this was the same Samuel Lightbound listed as both owner and occupier of the mill on the tithe apportionment of c.1843, and also in *Bagshaw's Cheshire Directory* of 1850, then Tranmere mill may have closed as an outcome of his death.

93. This oil painting of Tranmere mill is signed W. F. Crook and dated 1841. It shows this windmill to have been five storeys high and the tall chimney alongside the mill suggests it was equipped with a steam engine. (Courtesy of the Williamson Art Gallery and Museum)

94. This painting, by an unknown artist, shows a striking resemblance to a similar picture by W. F. Crook. It depicts Tranmere mill as it was when in working order in the early 1840s. (Courtesy of the Mills Archive Trust)

Whilst this mill was working Tranmere remained a predominantly rural and undeveloped area. By the date of demolition, the town was beginning to become more urbanised. A road called Mill Street was built next to the site of the mill, running between Borough Road and Church Road. Later on Mill Street was split into two sections; that off Borough Road retained the name Mill Street, whilst that off Church Road was called Mill Close. Tranmere mill was set some way back from Church Road and the site is now a little way down Mill Close, just north of the road itself. Four residential buildings, constructed in quite recent years, have been built on the northern side of Mill Close. The approximate site of the mill is covered by the most easterly of these two buildings.

5.2 Higher Bebington and Storeton Mills

The Higher Bebington area has a long established connection with windmills which spans many centuries. The final windmill to stand here, a four storey tower mill, was the last of a succession of mills built in this vicinity. Early post mills are said to have been recorded here during the latter half of the 14th century, according to Alsbury writing in *Fir-Bob Land.* He says that Thomas Hough was the miller in 1424. There is record of William Collye paying £2 rent to a Mr. Minshull for a "windye-millne" in Over Bebington in November 1644. This reference was listed in 'Sequestrators' Accounts for Wirral', published in the *Cheshire Sheaf* in July 1955. Mills have stood on both sides of Mount Road, in Higher Bebington and Storeton townships.

Storeton township holds some ancient sites when it comes to milling, for a windmill is listed here in an inquisition post mortem dated 1284. This is early when one considers that the first definite record of a windmill in England is in 1185. Bott writing in 'Cornmill Sites in Cheshire 1086-1850' reckoned this to be the earliest record of a windmill in Cheshire, although it is actually not so early as the Poulton Lancelyn windmill listed in Part 3 of this book, which he did not consider. Another early reference to a windmill at Storeton is a 1349 inquisition post mortem into the death of William de Lakene. This inquisition was printed in the *Cheshire Sheaf* in September 1956 and includes a "third part of a windmill, 12d.". This third share came through Sir Philip de Bamville Knight, the lord of Storeton, who died around 1283. He left a third of his manor to each of three daughters, one of them was Ellen, who married William de Lakene. Another was Agnes who married John de Becheton; she passed her share to their son Simon de Becheton in an indenture dated 1348, in which a mill is also mentioned. Simon de Becheton died in 1349, at which point his inquisition post mortem recorded that he held one third of Storeton, including the windmill there. Philip de Bamville's third daughter was Joan, she inherited the other third of Storeton, and married William de Stanley in 1282. Ultimately the entire manor became vested in the Stanley family.

A later reference to a windmill at Storeton is in the 1590 will of Thomas Gill, the miller of Bromborough. This will was published in the *Cheshire Sheaf* in October 1958 and states – "To Emme my wife and Robert my son his 3 leases viz. of Brombero mills and Storeton mill; also of Hawarden mills" A windmill is marked on the west side of Mount Road on Burdett's map of 1777 on an area labelled as "Storeton Heath". This was a post mill known as Storeton mill and it is also marked on Hunter's map of 1790. It survived into the early 19th century until succeeded by the Higher Bebington tower mill. Storeton mill, which directly preceded the tower mill at Higher Bebington, was worked by the Lightbound family from at least the 1760s.

95. Burdett's map predates the construction of Higher Bebington tower mill. The Lightbounds' Storeton post mill is marked on an area called "Storeton Heath".

Samuel Lightbound was listed as the miller on the manor court roll of 1772; he had been left Storeton mill by his father William Lightbound in a will dated 1767. He was also named as an executor of his brother's will in 1797, that brother being William Lightbound of Willaston mill, who had been left Willaston mill by their father in 1767. The Lightbound family are thought to have obtained the lease of this mill through marriage with the Hough family, who held a mill at Higher Bebington in the 15th century. Storeton mill was owned by the Stanley family of Hooton Hall for they held the manor of Storeton. It is frequently mentioned in the 4th Baronet Sir Rowland Stanley's account book for the period 1746-1751. The first reference is on 26th March 1746 when £2 10s. 0d. was "received of Humphrey Griffith in part of his…Rent for Storton Miln". Similarly on 18th November 1747 £3 0s. 0d. was "received of John Yates in part of Rent for Storton Mill". Both of these names continue to crop up in 1748, the name Yates also appears in 1749 and 1750. On June 11th 1748, Benjamin Tyrer was paid "for a Millstone for Storton Mill".

Writing on 'The Antiquities of Storeton' in 1897 the historian Edward Cox said, "On the south end of the quarry hill formerly stood the manor mill, now destroyed and almost forgotten. Some of the inhabitants have heard of it as a wooden mill built of oak timber, whose precise site there is now nothing to indicate". This is a reference to the Storeton post mill. There are three mill related field names in Storeton township. These fields, all named "Mill Hey" on the tithe map of 1840, lie next to one another, south of Storeton village and along the west side of Keepers' Lane. Although partially still in existence, they have been bisected by the M53. It is felt that they likely denote the approximate location of this post mill. It is hard to say how the later post mill was related to the very early references in this township and multiple sites must be present. A likely mill mound lies at the top and to the east of Keepers' Lane, a second potential site is identified as a crop mark and is west of Red Hill Road.

The last mill to stand here was on the Higher Bebington side of Mount Road. This Higher Bebington mill was a brick tower mill built during the early 19th century, most likely during the 1810s. Alsbury, writing in *Fir-Bob Land*, maintains that the mill was built in 1827 by a millwright of the name A. Ball, based on the evidence that he apparently "left his mark and the date on one of the beams in the mill". However, this seems somewhat too late and likely refers to repair work. This tower mill is marked on Greenwood's map of 1819, so it must have been built during the first two decades of the 19th century. The first edition Ordnance Survey map of c.1840 marks the Higher Bebington tower mill as "Storeton Hill Mill".

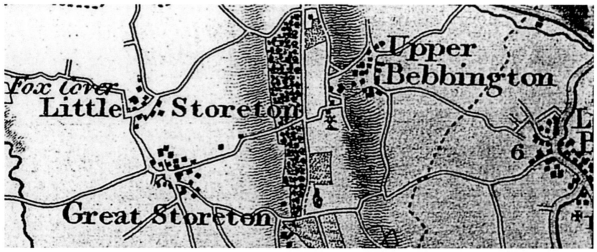

96. Greenwood's map shows the mill at Higher Bebington at its final site south of Village Road, thus proving it had been built by 1819.

As well as working the old post mill it was the Lightbounds who built and worked the tower mill during the first years of its existence. John Lightbound is listed as the mill's owner on the tithe apportionment of c.1844. Interestingly the plot which contained the windmill not only housed John Lightbound, but was also occupied by James Buck, Samuel Hardy, John Houldsworth and John Youde. These men were presumably additional workers. The Lightbounds were still working the mill in 1864. At this date *Morris & Co.'s Directory of Cheshire* lists William Lighbound as a "farmer and miller" at this site. Later on in the latter half of the 19th century, they rented the mill to another family, the Johnsons, who went on to obtain the freehold in the 1870s. It was they who worked it until closure. The mill property included granaries, stables and other storage buildings. Several two storey buildings of local stone once adjoined the mill tower. As well as grain from local fields, further grain was imported. The stone floor of the mill was the third floor and it contained six pairs of millstones. Both flour and animal fodder were produced here.

This mill featured a wooden windshaft through which the sails were mortised, yet the chain wheel was of cast iron by the 1890s. Many of the gears were composed of cast iron sections attached to a wooden framework, showing this tower mill to have been a product of the industrialised era. During the 1870s a portable steam engine, the *Wirral Lassie*, was used to drive the mill to complement the use of wind power. The success of this venture led to the installation of a stationary steam engine in its own engine house c.1880. The engine house chimney was almost as tall as the mill itself and stood until after the Second World War; it had been derelict for many years prior to demolition.

The mill worked until c.1901, some sources state that the mill worked further into the first decade of the 20th century. However, the mill was no longer working when Mitford Abraham visited in 1903. Mitford Abraham said the reason behind the closure was – "owing principally to the fact that the miller had some steam mills built in Birkenhead". In *Kelly's Directory* of 1902 for Cheshire under "Millers" there is a Samuel Johnson listed at "Mill Brow, Higher Bebington" using both wind and steam power. He is also listed at "22-38 Livingstone Street, Birkenhead" as a steam miller, suggesting Mitford Abraham's statement to be correct. In later directories the address at Mill Brow continues to be included, alongside that at Livingstone Street, but I would assume that by this point all work had been transferred to the Birkenhead steam mill. Some years after closure when Mitford Abraham visited the mill he recorded that – "The machinery is complete, but the roof and stage are in a very ruinous state; part of the stage has entirely disappeared". After it finished work the mill was used as a store. No tenant was prepared to rent the mill for further use, even at a rent of only £5 a year.

After over a decade unused the sails were considered a hazard and were taken down around the time of the First World War. It is said that the aged wood was extremely tough and this meant the sails proved very troublesome to saw through. Writing in *Cheshire Life* in 1952 Eastwood said that – "the sails are now stored within the mill, together with the vast grindstones and ponderous wooden machinery". During the 1930s efforts were made to try and preserve the building. The *Liverpool Daily Post* ran an article in September 1933 which said "The fate of an historic mill in Higher Bebington Village is in the balance. Appeals for its preservation have been made by the Society for the Preservation of Rural England and by residents...The Council is anxious to preserve it but a considerable sum would have to be spent on repairs and supervision and maintenance". Nothing ever came of the plans, presumably due to the prohibitive cost of preservation and later on the outbreak of the Second World War. During the war the mill saw a new function as a look out post. Years of neglect and a lack of maintenance took their toll on the building which gradually deteriorated in condition; the cap was blown off completely in 1933.

97. Higher Bebington mill when it was in working order in
1897, with sailcloths in place upon the common sails.

The mill was owned by the last miller, Harry Johnson, up until his death in 1947. It was then sold to a builders firm run by the Williams brothers; they used the outbuildings for storage purposes. One of the brothers, Reg Williams, was a former Mayor of Bebington. Eastwood said in *Cheshire Life* in 1952 that "Harry Johnson died five years ago, and Mr. Williams well remembers Harry complaining as a young man because his father would call him out at all hours to get the sails moving when the wind was blowing up". The Williams later sold the mill to another builders firm, probably around 1966. By this time the mill was in a very dilapidated and dangerous state. This firm were unfortunately responsible for the mill's demolition. The mill was listed as a building of "special historical and architectural interest"; for this reason advanced notice of the intended demolition had to be given to the local council. The council examined the structure, but due to its excessively poor condition no preservation order was made and demolition was allowed to go ahead in 1968. Alsbury writing in 1969, shortly after the mill's destruction said, "there were many tearful eyes among old and young alike when demolition started".

98. Higher Bebington mill is seen standing in Mill Brow, either whilst still in use in the 1890s, or soon after it stopped working c.1901. (Courtesy of the Mills Archive Trust)

99. This photograph shows Higher Bebington mill around the time that it fell out of use at the turn of the 20th century. The chimney alongside the mill was associated with the steam engine which was installed around 1880. (Courtesy of the Mills Archive Trust)

100. In this photograph of Higher Bebington mill, the endless chain used to rotate the cap can be seen hanging alongside the tower. (Courtesy of the Mills Archive Trust)

101. Higher Bebington mill c.1910, less than a decade after it fell out of use and when the common sails were still in place. (Courtesy of Ian Boumphrey)

102. Higher Bebington mill and cottages are seen perched above the quarry at Higher Bebington c.1910.

103. Higher Bebington mill around the time of the First World War. The stage is in a very ruinous condition and the engine house chimney may be seen behind the mill itself. (Courtesy of Ian Boumphrey)

104. Mill Terrace which still stands off School Lane is seen in front of Higher Bebington mill prior to 1914, at which point the sails were taken down. (Courtesy of Ian Boumphrey)

105. This photograph, taken by the mill enthusiast Donald Muggeridge, shows that by 1936 Higher Bebington mill had already fallen into a ruinous condition. (Courtesy of Special Collections and Archives, Templeman Library, University of Kent)

106. In 1960, eight years before it was demolished, Higher Bebington mill was in extremely poor condition and many of its associated buildings had already been pulled down. (Courtesy of the Mills Archive Trust)

The demolition of this mill was clearly a great loss. Its destruction was an act of vandalism which clearly lacked foresight. One would have hoped that the people responsible would have known better only forty five years ago. The mill was a dearly loved landmark of Higher Bebington. Unfruitful attempts to save it were made by various local groups from the 1930s onwards. Despite some seventy years since closure the building still contained much milling machinery. I do not know what became of it, but suspect it was simply disposed of.

Williams and Crompton writing in 1976, nearly a decade after this mill's demolition, noted with respect to the mill's outbuildings – "Parts of these buildings survived the 1968 demolition and a millstone lies close to the site". Even these remains have now gone, as the area has been redeveloped. The site of the mill is at the end of Mill Brow. A group of four modern bungalows occupy the plot where the mill and associated buildings once stood. A few walls of the local white sandstone still surround this plot and these must have once enclosed the windmill. The orderly modern housing is a far cry from the ruinous relics of a previous age which covered this area throughout much of the 1960s. Opposite the bungalows stands "Millside Villa"; originally called "Mill House", this house was built for the Johnsons, the last family to work the mill.

107. The houses which occupy the site of Higher Bebington mill have a wall of local white sandstone at the rear of their back gardens.

108. Mill Terrace in 2008; this row of houses once stood in front of Higher Bebington mill.

5.3 Bromborough Mills

The site of Bromborough watermill is a truly ancient one. A watermill probably stood in this area before the Norman Conquest, for a mill which formed part of the "Manor of Estham" and which was held by Earl Hugh, was listed in the Domesday survey of 1086. The survey, which was translated by Tait in *The Domesday Survey of Cheshire*, recorded that in Eastham "There is a mill, 2 radmans and a priest" ("*ibi molinum et ii radman et unus presbyter*"). Earl Hugh was Hugh d'Avranches, one of the first Norman Earls of Chester. Before the Normans lay claim to English estates, Eastham manor had been held by Earl Edwin, the last Anglo-Saxon Earl of Mercia, he was dispossessed on his death in 1071. It seems probable that the mill mentioned was located in Bromborough, for in Domesday times the manor of Eastham was an especially large one, including all the land which eventually fell within Bromborough township. An Anglo-Saxon mill could well have occupied the same site as the mill which existed into more recent years, although with no archaeological evidence to that effect, this cannot be proved. The first probable evidence for a mill at the known site in Bromborough is in the 13th century, when the mill was the property of St. Werburgh's Abbey, Chester.

A Latin charter from the abbey, dated 1313 refers to *"molendinum de Bromburgh"*. A translation printed in the Chartulary of St. Werburgh's Abbey as published by the Chetham Society states – "Grant by William, son of William Lancelyn, to Thomas II, abbot of Chester, of liberty of digging in his land of Poulton (Lancelyn) and Bebington beyond The Pool in Poultondale, and of making ditches...to drain away the excess of water coming down to the abbot's mill or mills...also liberty of digging in the said lands stones for the needs of the mills". Another early reference is in a 1461 arbitration document involving Roger Lancelyn. The mill is listed on a rent roll of 1398 for St Werburgh's Abbey, at which point the rent was £10 per year. On the dissolution of the abbey in 1540 the newly formed Chester Cathedral assumed possession of the mill. Rent was paid to these religious institutions by a succession of tenant millers who worked the mill over the centuries. The manor of Bromborough later passed to Sir Richard Cotton and then to the Hardware family. A quotation published by Mortimer in his *The History of the Hundred of Wirral* relates that in the latter half of the 16th century "Henry Hardware had the old manor-house called Brombro' Court, the demesne, the water mills, and a wood...valued at £9 per annum".

The last incarnation of this mill continued to work into living memory, right up until 1940. The site of Bromborough mill was in the valley of the River Dibbin, at the point near where the river flows under Spital Road. The mill and associated buildings were built along the base of a sandstone outcrop. This forms a prominent rock face on the east side of the road. A sandstone dam was built across the Dibbin nearby and the water collected in a large mill pool. Connah writing in the 21st Annual report of the Bromborough Society, said of the dam – "the present representative...is a nineteenth century reconstruction. During the nineteenth century also the pool was enlarged and retaining walls built along all its sides". Before the construction of Bromborough Dock the Dibbin at this point was heavily influenced by high spring tides, leading to influxes of tidal water from Bromborough Pool.

Indeed, the tide continued to influence the site when the dock gates were open, for many years after Bromborough Dock was built. The tidal behaviour of the area may have been detrimental; Mitford Abraham wrote that "owing to the tide backing up...the mill is stopped working for about four hours every tide". However, the semi-tidal nature of the Dibbin did raise the level of the mill pool and so this was to an extent a tide mill, which benefitted from the tidal influx. Indeed, Connah commented that – "Mr Ellis, the last miller, claims it could only be used when the tide was going out and so the miller often stayed up all night to catch the tide". The fact that the mill was operated at different times in order to make use of the tide seems to prove that Bromborough mill was worked as a tide mill. Miss Bird, born at Bromborough mill in the mid-19th century and whose recollections were published in the *Birkenhead Advertiser* in 1944, stated that high flood tides would be harnessed with saltwater impounded and subsequently released once the tide began to go out.

Although it occupied an ancient site the mill was rebuilt numerous times. The last mill to stand here was, according to Mitford Abraham, a "rebuilt structure of the eighteenth century", a view also shared by Connah who stated "how many reconstructions took place...is impossible to imagine. Thus in the twentieth century the actual remaining buildings of the water-mill were mainly of the eighteenth and nineteenth centuries". The oldest building on site was probably a brick built structure known as the "old sack house". This likely dated from the late 17th century and adjoined the mill building on the south side. The sandstone built mill house stood next to the mill itself and was of 18th century origin. The miller lived here until c.1900, but it was later converted into two cottages. A brick built extension, probably of the 19th century, adjoined the mill house; this was once used as an office. Next to the mill house was a sandstone barn. This was also of 18th century construction and was once used as a stable.

The watermill itself was a large building constructed from the local red sandstone. There were three storeys and a cellar, whilst inside there were four pairs of millstones on the ground floor; these were removed some years prior to demolition. The first and second floors were used as storage space. According to Connah the milling machinery was from sometime in the 19th century for he said, "none of the milling installations...were earlier than the last century" when writing in 1949. The mill had a seventeen foot undershot waterwheel nearly four feet wide. This was housed in a partitioned off section of the cellar, separated from the cellar proper by a sandstone wall. This cellar was partially cut from the bedrock. A sluice gate operated from the cellar controlled the flow of water to the wheel. Connah dated the wheel to "some time in the period 1869-1882" and described it as "heavy teak timbers with iron jointings cast at Lanceley's and Son, Chester". The primarily wooden construction of this waterwheel demonstrates how long wood prevailed in the construction of milling machinery, even after the industrial revolution.

The mill was worked by many families, some of whom worked it for only a short amount of time. However, other families produced generations of millers. In several cases a single family worked the mill for a century or more. One of these families was the Gill family who are first recorded to have worked the mill in 1571. They worked it for over a century up until 1693. The will of Thomas Gill, dating to 1590, showed him to be extremely affluent; the debts owed to him at the time of his death amounted to the enormous sum of £841 0s. 6d. Henry Hardware of Mouldsworth and Bromborough Courthouse was renting the mill to Robert Gill for £2 in 1610, as mentioned in a rental of that year. Henry Hardware owned the mill from at least 1557. He died in 1615, at which point the "manor of Brumborowe with appurtenances in Brumborowe & of a water grain mill" were listed in his inquisition post mortem, as published in *Cheshire Inquisitions Post Mortem: Stuart Period 1603-1660*.

In 1777 the mill was leased to the Ellis family of Great Barrow for ninety nine years, by Thomas Penlington of Denbigh. The rent was £30 a year to be paid in two instalments on 29th September and 25th of March. The Penlingtons were responsible for "repairs to mill, buildings, wears and watercourses and 3 pairs of Mill Stones and also a Boulting or Dressing Mill together with proper Machinery and Geer for the working of such Mill Stones and Boulting Mill". Interestingly the lease also mentions that there was a kiln for drying oats. The Ellis family worked the mill for over one hundred and fifty years, right up until its final closure in 1940. William Ellis and Joseph Ellis were both listed as millers here in *Morris & Co.'s Directory of Cheshire* of 1864. In 1777, the same year the watermill was originally leased to them, the family constructed a four storey brick tower mill at the same site.

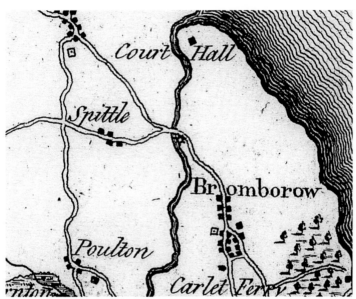

109. Burdett marked Bromborough watermill on the river south of "Court Hall" on his map of 1777. The windmill had not been built when he completed his survey.

The windmill stood upon the sandstone outcrop behind the watermill, but was demolished with explosives in 1878, having become dangerous. The Bromborough Society reported in their *Bromborough in Times Past* that the mill worked "for just over 90 years", suggesting it fell out of use in the late 1860s. Mitford Abraham said that "The man who was entrusted with its demolition has several times explained how the whole mill was blown into the air several feet, and then falling to the ground, fell to pieces". Some of the bricks from the windmill were used to build a long outbuilding in 1878, this building was later converted into a row of eight terraced cottages. During the construction of Mill Road two millstones from the windmill were discovered. These were later placed in the grounds of Bromborough Library, then based at Stanhope House. Unfortunately their whereabouts is now unknown. A house was built on the outcrop where the windmill stood in 1910. The driveway to this house from Mill Lane predates the building itself and was re-opened after a period of disuse. When it was cleared this drive was found to be well cobbled and it is retained by a wall of sandstone blocks, which may still be seen. The track was almost certainly once the route to the windmill and associated cottages.

BROMBOROUGH MILL,

_____189

Dear Sir,

We beg to quote you our present prices, as under :—

Large Corn	per 240 lbs.
Crushed Corn	,, ,, ,,
Cinquantina Corn	,, ,, ,,
Odessa Corn	,, ,, ,,
Round Corn	,, ,, ,,
Indian Meal	,, ,, ,,
Pea Meal	, ,, ,,
Barley Meal	,, ,, ,,
Split English Beans	,, ,, ,,
Split Egyptian Beans	,, 60 ,,
White Oats	,, 45 ,,
Yellow Oats	,, ,, ,,
Crushed Oats	,, ,, ,,
Ground Oats	,, ,, ,,
Common Bran	,, 20 ,,
Broad Bran	,, ,, ,,
Barley	,, 60 ,,
Dari	,, 240 ,,
Wheat	,, ,, ,,
Fourths	,, ,, ,,
Sharps	,, ,, ,,
Dog Biscuits	,, 112 ,,
Trenchstone	,, 240 ,,
Flour, Trieste	,, 280 ,,
No. 1 Mill	,, ,, ,,
No. 2 Mill	,, ,, ,,
No. 3 Mill	,, ,, ,,

Yours truly,

ELLIS BROS.

ALL PRICES QUOTED SUBJECT, TO MARKET FLUCTUATIONS, AND TO BEING UNSOLD ON RECEIPT OF REPLY. TERMS NETT CASH.

110. A piece of paperwork of the 1890s from Bromborough mill. This sheet could evidently be filled in with the current prices and gives some idea of the range of products offered in the late 19th century.

One of the earliest maps to show Bromborough mill with clarity is the Mainwaring estate map dated c.1755. The watermill is shown on Burdett's map of 1777; the windmill was built in the same year as Burdett's map was published, but is not shown for the survey was conducted some years earlier. Both the watermill and the windmill are marked on Greenwood's map of 1819, they are also shown on Bryant's map of 1831. The watermill and windmill are then shown on the Bromborough township tithe map of 1840. There were several plots which were in the joint occupation of various members of the Ellis family; Charles Ellis, Robert Ellis and William Ellis. Plot 58 included the "water-mill and steam-mill", whilst plot 54 contained the "wind-mill, cottage and garden". The owner of the land was Reverend James Mainwaring, who in the mid-19th century was in possession of virtually the whole township of Bromborough. James Mainwaring had purchased the Hardware family's property in Bromborough in 1771. One of the conditions of the original 1777 lease to the Ellis family was that – "Charles Mainwaring and family to be granted toll-free milling...and toll-free oat-drying in kiln".

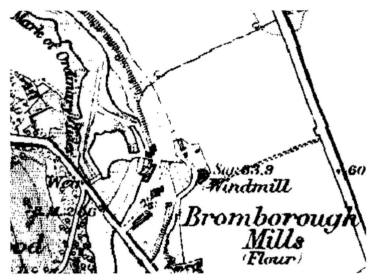

111. The windmill and watermill are both shown on this Ordnance Survey map of c.1875 and are called "Bromborough Mills". (Courtesy of and Copyright Old-Maps and Ordnance Survey)

In 1835 a steam engine was installed at the mill by Fawcett Preston & Co. of Liverpool, thus providing an alternative means of power. The engine was a beam engine with an eleven foot flywheel and eighteen inch stroke. This was housed in its own red sandstone engine house which was constructed next to the mill, on the north side. Adjustable gears were provided so that the millstones could be coupled to the steam engine, when there was a lack of water available. Mitford Abraham claimed that the mill had been reduced to animal feed production by 1903. He stated that – "as there is no flour made here now, steam is never used". This was presumably as it was not economically viable to use steam when only milling cattle feed. In the late 19th century, before the mill was relegated to cattle feed production, a flat boat called *Two Brothers* was used to bring sacks of corn to the mill. This boat had been built at Northwich in 1825. It could hold two hundred sacks of corn and was brought up river to the mill, having been brought across the Mersey from Liverpool Landing Stage.

Lever Brothers bought the land on which the mill stood in 1905. In 1910 they constructed a railway embankment, forty feet high, across the back of the site, to the north of the watermill building. The embankment destroyed the windmill cottages which had been built on the hill at the same time as the windmill itself. The rest of the buildings survived unscathed, although the beam engine was removed from its engine house around this time. The embankment ran across the Dibbin and a large concrete culvert was provided for the water which came past the mill dam. The mill never worked via water power following the construction of the embankment. According to Connah the railway "totally altered the nature of the site…the waterway past the mill was completely blocked rendering the waterwheel useless". It was not the original intention that the mill would be affected and it was hoped that it could continue to operate by water power. Construction work started some way downstream with forty foot piles driven into the river bed. A solid foundation on which to construct the culvert could not be found and work slowly moved upstream towards the mill. A rocky outcrop was eventually discovered at the point where the embankment was built. A secondary culvert now needed to be built for the leat if the mill was to work as a watermill, but this did not happen.

112. This photograph predates the demolition of Bromborough windmill in 1878, and could even date from the late 1860s. That is when this mill fell out of use and sailcloths seem to be in place on this photograph suggesting it was still working. (Courtesy of Birkenhead Reference Library)

The mill continued to work from this point onwards using an oil engine housed in the old steam engine house; the waterwheel was now utterly useless. Operation continued in this manner for another thirty years, up until 1940. Although not a major output, it would seem that some flour may have been produced, even towards the end of the mill's life. *Bromborough in Times Past* says that up until 1940 "Mr Ellis was a familiar figure, still delivering orders by horse and cart; local residents recall going to the mill for flour and barm for home baking, for corn for poultry and for pigeon peas". This refers to Eric Ellis, the last miller at Bromborough. He was born in 1891 and finally ended his family's almost two century connection with the mill in 1946, six years after closure. The oil engine remained at the time of the 1949 demolition.

113. Bromborough watermill and windmill are seen prior to the windmill's demolition in 1878. In the foreground a boat may be seen, which would have been navigated up the River Dibbin from the Mersey. (Courtesy of the Mills Archive Trust)

114. Another photograph of the watermill and windmill at Bromborough prior to 1878. The building adjoining the watermill on the right hand side is the "old sack house" and further to the right is the mill house.

115. This view shows Bromborough watermill in 1905. The railway embankment constructed some years later destroyed the windmill cottages, which may be seen to the left of the engine house chimney. (Courtesy of The Heswall Society)

116. An extremely rare internal photograph of Mitford Abraham's shows a set of millstones and a chute to feed them with grain within Bromborough watermill, probably c.1905. (Courtesy of The Heswall Society)

117. These disused millstones had formerly been employed inside Bromborough windmill and were still to be seen c.1910, over three decades after its demolition. (Courtesy of The Heswall Society)

118. This photograph shows Bromborough mill and associated buildings in the late 1920s. The building on the far right was a terraced row of cottages built using bricks from the demolished windmill. (Courtesy of Ian Boumphrey)

119. This elevated view of the early 1930s was probably taken from the railway embankment and shows the extent of the mill pool and weir at Spital Dam. The terraced cottages, which came almost up to Spital Road, were demolished in 1936. (Courtesy of Ian Boumphrey)

After closure in 1940 the watermill was used as a store. It was not long before the mill and its associated buildings began to deteriorate. There were two major groups of buildings on opposite sides of a trackway which led off Spital Road. On the east side of the track was a cluster of buildings which consisted of the watermill, "old sack house" and engine house. On the western side was the sandstone mill house, with its brick extension. There was also the barn and row of cottages. The first building on site to be demolished was the row of cottages, which were pulled down in 1936. By 1937 the "old sack house" had also been demolished and the mill house partially destroyed. In 1949 the rest of the buildings on site were demolished by Lever Brothers, who still owned the land. This was a sad end to a site of great antiquity.

During the main demolition in 1949 Graham Connah carried out extensive research on the building. He was able to enter the watermill building, including the cellars. The undershot wheel and some machinery remained at the date of demolition, but all remaining machinery was quickly destroyed. Demolition of the watermill began in March 1949 at which point he commented – "Spital mill is being pulled down by Levers. Lady Leverhulme is President of the Bromborough Society which has as its main aim to preserve ancient buildings and yet Lord Leverhulme pulls down Spital mill, I do not understand at all". The engine house attached to the watermill had already been demolished at this point, probably earlier in 1949. The mill was taken down from the top and by mid-April 1949 only the first floor and cellar remained. The wheelhouse and waterwheel within the cellar interested Graham Webster of the Grosvenor Museum who said of the wheel – "It should be salvaged if possible and put under cover"; unfortunately this did not occur. It is to Connah that we owe a lot of the information included in this section, for without him many details of the building would have been irretrievably lost.

The predecessor of Spital Road did not span the Dibbin and mill pool as it does today; the road only took this route when a bridge was constructed across the mill pool in the late 18th century. Formerly the route taken ran around the back of the watermill. It crossed the leat to a marshy area, now under Levers' embankment, by a stone bridge. This was an important route in its day, for it could well have formed the main link between Chester and Woodside. During demolition of a bridge at the mill this old road was discovered and excavated by Connah. Underneath more recent deposits the road took the form of a cobbled causeway some ten and a half feet wide. This could be traced for a considerable distance of some forty three feet. The causeway exposed was at least early 18th century in construction, but likely followed a route of even greater antiquity.

120. Bromborough mill had been largely demolished by the 15th April 1949 when this was what remained of the ground floor. In the foreground is a temporary railway used to remove salvaged stone. (Courtesy of Graham Connah)

121. The corner of Bromborough mill as seen from the outside on 15th April 1949. To the left is the mill pool and in the background Lever Brothers's railway embankment. (Courtesy of Graham Connah)

122. This is what remained of the ground floor of Bromborough mill on 30th April 1949. To the right of the mill, the ruinous remains of the old mill house can be seen. (Courtesy of Graham Connah)

The site of Bromborough mill is now hardly recognisable as the ancient site where a watermill was demolished over sixty five years ago. Most of the area where the mill and its associated buildings stood has been extensively levelled and now forms the grounds of a sewage pumping station on Spital Road. The pumping station covers some of the area occupied by the buildings, whilst the rest of the area is now grassed over. The mill pool once formed a huge reserve of water which came right up to the mill. That is no longer the case and it seems to have been partially in-filled after demolition. The demolition process was very thorough. The only feature remaining at the site is the 19th century mill dam, which still blocks the Dibbin. It retains a vestige of the mill pool, a mere fraction of its former size. Some sandstone retaining walls, also of the 19th century, line the Dibbin just downstream of the weir.

It may seem that the mill's life entirely ended in 1949, but a rather interesting development occurred thirty years later, in 1979. In that year excavations took place at the mill's site in order for drains to be laid. During the digging of one of the trenches the workmen discovered the remains of the waterwheel, along with the main axle and pit wheel. When in use the waterwheel was partially below ground level, in a blocked off portion of the cellar. The mill pool side of the building was considerably lower than that which faced the cliff behind. The most easterly part of the pond has been in-filled and the ground where the mill stood levelled. For this to occur most of the cellar could have been in-filled, whilst at least half of the waterwheel was left in place. It would seem that the workmen simply buried the waterwheel, in its original situation, whilst clearing the site. It is also the case that some walls of the cellar must still exist beneath ground level, maybe one day they will be exposed again?

We are very fortunate that Allan Alsbury recorded many of the artefacts whilst they were on site. He used the decayed remains unearthed to produce a wealth of diagrams which record a vast range of data on all dimensions of the mill's main drive system. The most substantial find was the iron axle, the nine foot diameter pit wheel still remaining at one end. Further down the axle were the two three and a half foot diameter hubs from the waterwheel. These had once held the wooden spokes in position. The underground conditions cannot have been favourable for preserving the wooden parts of the wheel. Although the wheel was presumably complete when buried it would seem that many of the parts decayed entirely.

123. The main axle from Bromborough mill as excavated in 1979. This had the pit wheel attached at one end and also the hubs associated with the undershot waterwheel. (Courtesy of the Bromborough Society)

Sufficient remains were found for accurate drawings of the entire waterwheel to be made. One of the most interesting parts to be found was one of the iron castings which held the wooden rim of the wheel to the radial spokes; the words "H. LANCELEY CHESTER" were apparently still distinguishable. At least one of these castings was found with pieces of the rim, a spoke and paddles still attached. Various well preserved sections of the wooden rim were also found, with paddles still in place. Then there was the iron band, which supported the spokes at an intermediate position between the rim and axle. Even the bearings which supported the main axle were discovered. In short, a good example of every part of the waterwheel was found, probably approximately a century old at this point.

The unfortunate thing is that now, forty years later, I have been unable to trace any of the parts. I know that the main axle and pit wheel left the site, after remaining where they were found for some years. According to *Bromborough in Times Past* it was, "acquired by the Rural Preservation Society of Lark Lane, Liverpool, who had it taken to a field site off Aigburth Road, Liverpool. It was then cleared of rust by sandblasting and given coats of preservative paint. It was to be placed with other archaeological exhibits and to be used as an adventure-play area feature". It seems strange that this artefact was removed from Wirral; surely it could have been acquired by a local society or the council? For it to have been placed over the road in the Dibbin Valley seems a much more fitting end. As for the other parts of the waterwheel; the iron castings, bearings and remaining woodwork, there does not seem to be any information regarding what happened to them. They may simply have been disposed of from the site, or maybe they remain preserved in somebody's private collection.

In 2008 further changes occurred at the site of the mill. The site was put up for sale and sometime later building work began for the construction of a children's nursery. The nursery was to be situated behind the much reduced mill pool, at a site adjacent to the sewage pumping station and site of the former mill. This area had been overgrown and wild ever since the mill's demolition. It was formerly covered by the mill pool and had been for many hundreds of years. Connah said that the mill pool was – "possibly the only surviving part of the fourteenth century mill constructed by the Abbot of St. Werburgh's, Chester". According to The Wirral Society, writing in *Wirral Matters* of Autumn 2008 – "A delay was requested on the start of building work as the site is (or was) one of special archaeological interest. The request was ignored". The site has now been built on, drowned in bricks and mortar. The disturbed area extends all the way back to Levers' embankment. This building work has effectively destroyed the last undisturbed area of the ancient site of Bromborough mill. Measures were taken to enclose and further reduce the former mill pond, which still used to flood the built on area during heavy rain. One relic from this mill may still be seen in the Dell, Port Sunlight. This is a large millstone which appears to be a running stone and has now been relegated to covering a sewer. According to Eric Ellis it was removed from Bromborough mill in 1927, but had not been used since c.1890.

124. The 19th century weir which still crosses the
River Dibbin at the site of Bromborough mill.

125. A nursery being constructed on land once occupied by the mill pool in 2008. The remnants of the old pool may be seen in the foreground.

126. The pumping station which now occupies the site of Bromborough mill. The windmill stood on the outcrop visible to the right.

127. A large millstone last used in Bromborough mill around 1890 and now in the Dell, Port Sunlight.

5.4 Raby Mill

Raby mill was a watermill located at the northern end of Raby Mere. The mere is a man-made pool, intentionally created to power a mill. This site is likely of considerably antiquity, for records of a mill in the township go back to at least the 14th century. The present mere could well have been the power source for the ancient mill. A rent roll of 1398 relating to Henry Sutton, who was the abbot of St Werburgh's, gives rents payable to the abbey from various locations and was published in the *Cheshire Sheaf* in August 1912. Under Raby it is listed that "Hugh de Holes held the mill by a free rent of 14s". This indicates a watermill associated with the former monastic estate at Raby. It is difficult to say how this ancient site related to the later mill, which appears to have been primarily 17th century in origin. But it could certainly be that the later mill represented a rebuilding on the original site, the mere itself being of monastic origin.

William Dunsterfielde is listed at Raby on a list of debts contained in the will, dated 1590, of Thomas Gill, miller of Bromborough. Brownbill's transcription of the will was published in the *Cheshire Sheaf* in November 1958, in which it was suggested that William Dunsterfielde "was probably the miller of Raby Water Mill and built part of the existing building". The Dunsterfieldes were a wealthy family, some members of whom were bailiffs to the Earls of Shrewbury. William Dunsterfielde was likely not the miller himself, he was the lessee of the building from the Earl of Shrewsbury, and sub-leased it himself to a tenant miller. Blakeley Road is built across the top of the mill dam and the ruinous 17th century watermill is still hidden away, beneath the road level. The situation of the mill, below the head of water in the pool, meant that it could be worked by an overshot waterwheel. This was a small mill built of local red sandstone and the last incarnation fell into disuse during the 1880s, probably in the latter half of that decade.

Raby mill is marked on Burdett's map of 1777, Greenwood's map of 1819 and Bryant's map of 1831. Ralph Langley may have been the miller here around the turn of the 18th century. He was a resident of Raby township and his occupation was given as a miller on his will, dated 1700. The tithe apportionment of c.1846 informs us that Richard Ghee was the miller at that point; he was also listed as a corn miller in *Bagshaw's Cheshire Directory* of 1850. The tithe apportionment further states that the mill was owned by the Earl of Shrewsbury. The Earls of Shrewsbury had acquired the manor of Raby through marriage with the Troutbeck family. It had descended to the Troutbecks by marriage with the Holes family, who held the manor by the late 14th century. A later Earl of Shrewsbury still owned the mill in 1903 when Mitford Abraham said "Although...what woodwork remains is always in a sodden state it is said the Earl of Shrewsbury and Talbot still insists on the ruin being insured against fire". The mill was in the ownership of the Talbot family who were the

Earls of Shrewsbury for some centuries. Indeed, Beazley writing in the *Cheshire Sheaf* in July 1909 stated that – "At the North end of the ruined watermill is a plate within a moulding…In the upper part there appears to have been an animal passant…no doubt a talbot or hunting dog, the badge of Talbots".

128. Bryant marked "Raby Mill" at the north end of Raby Mere and called Raby Mere Road, now intersected by the M53, "Water Mill Lane".

The miller here in 1857 was still Richard Gee, who was listed as such in the *Post Office Directory of Cheshire* in that year. *Slater's Directory of Cheshire and Liverpool* for 1883 gives two millers here. One of these was William Gee, a predecessor of whom is listed on the tithe apportionment c.1846. The other miller was Joseph Williamson. The Williamson family obtained the mill from the Gee family by marriage and worked it during the latter half of the 19th century, from at least the later 1860s, up until its closure in the 1880s. After it finished work the mill was left to decay; Mitford Abraham writing in 1903 said that "it is a pity to see such a picturesque little object falling into ruin so quickly as it is". The roof was still extant when Mitford Abraham visited the site, although it was "in a very dilapidated condition". The mill was an ancient building and according to Mitford Abraham – "Over the massive doorway there is a stone slab which used to bear the date 1601, together with some initials – DIA". Beazley interpreted this much worn plate differently and suggested Mitford Abraham had been misled; he stated that it likely bore the initials "IT", a reference to John Talbot who died in 1611. Yet another opinion is offered in *Neston: Stone Age to Steam Age*, published over a century after this stone became illegible. Here it is suggested the initials were "JAD" and referred to John and Alice Dunsterfielde, who had married in 1597.

Of the milling machinery Mitford Abraham said that "inside not much of the machinery, except the two pairs of stones and the 'overshot' wheel, now remain". This small mill probably contained no more than two pairs of stones whilst operational. After the milling of cereals stopped the mill was used to grind files by some metal merchants under the name of Collins. Pat O'Brien writing in *Around Bebington* relates that they brought cartloads of files to the mill, to grind them by water power. This new purpose presumably required additional machinery to be coupled to the waterwheel. The mill ceased to be used for this function when a steam factory became available to the firm in Birkenhead. The grinding of files had presumably come to an end by the 1890s, by which point the mill was already abandoned.

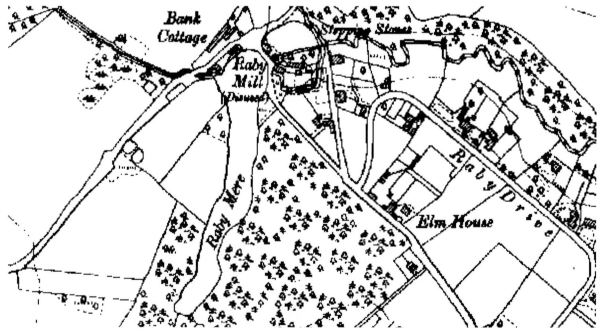

129. Raby mill is listed as "disused" on this Ordnance Survey map of c.1910. (Courtesy of and Copyright Old-Maps and Ordnance Survey)

When the mill had ceased to work the Williamson family set up some tea gardens in the grounds of their home, the "Mill House". This building is situated above the level of the mill on Blakeley Road. The two storey house has later additions, but is certainly 17th century in origin. The family ran the tea gardens for some decades and also hired out boats on the mere, which were introduced in the early 20th century. In *Slater's Directory* of 1902 Joseph Williamson was no longer a miller, but was listed as a – "refreshment rooms keeper and boat owner, Raby mere". Writing in *The Story of Bromborough* in 1964 Anderson said "the charming mill-house still stands and serves tea to stray visitors in its romantic little garden". Since 1984 the mere has only been used for fishing and most of the lake's perimeter is inaccessible unless you are permitted to fish the waters. According to Anderson, one of the datestones from the mill "inscribed 'WI 1791' has been set in a garden wall overlooking the Mere". Attempts to trace this relic have been unsuccessful and it is no longer to be found in any obvious wall. Edward Cox stated that this datestone could be seen at the mill itself in 1894 when he observed that "several dates are still to be seen on the pitiful heap which now represents the old mill". Other datestones seen at this time were from 1690 and 1704.

130. This photograph of Raby mill may date back as far as the early 1870s and shows the mill whilst it was still at work. The doorway, with a man standing next to it, gave access to the wheelhouse. (Courtesy of Ian Boumphrey)

131. Raby mill in a disused state in the late 1890s, the small size of the building is very evident. Above the doorway, a stone plate can be seen, which was said to be dated 1601. (Courtesy of Ian Boumphrey)

132. This is a scarce internal photograph taken within Raby mill. The cluttered interior suggests the mill was out of use and this view probably dates from the 1890s. (Courtesy of Birkenhead Reference Library)

133. This photograph likely dates from the early 20th century, by which point Raby mill had already fallen out of use. The roof can be seen to be in a state of disrepair. (Courtesy of the Mills Archive Trust)

134. Raby mill was little more than a ruin in this view c.1915. The roofing tiles had been dismantled by around 1910, although some roof beams were still in place at this point. (Courtesy of Ian Boumphrey)

135. This photograph shows the extremely overgrown front of Raby mill around 1920. At the right-hand side of the building, the wheelhouse may be seen containing the overshot wheel. (Courtesy of Ian Boumphrey)

136. Blakeley Road and Raby Mere in the early 20th century. Opposite the white wooden building was the mechanism to regulate water to the waterwheel. A connecting rod which was linked to a sluice gate can be seen extending down from the wall. (Courtesy of Ian Boumphrey)

As previously stated, the mill dam is represented by Blakeley Road, at the point where it crosses the head of the lake. The stream which has been dammed is a small one, which runs north from a point near Willaston. Most interestingly, it would seem that a second stream once fed the mere and this must have assisted in the formation of such a large pool. This second stream runs from the north east near Thornton Hough and passes through a wooded river valley, Foxes Wood, south of Thornton Common Road. The wood has been bisected by the M53 and in the section to the east of the motorway, a substantial artificial channel has been dug for about a third of a mile, parallel to the stream.

At the most westerly end of this channel a sandstone dam has been constructed across the stream, which remains in place to this day. Further worked sandstone blocks can be seen nearby, displaced within the watercourse. The dam evidently diverted a significant amount of water into the channel. Now dry, this channel would once have been significantly deeper, but has accumulated decades or centuries of organic debris. The stream drops down as the valley gets deeper; ultimately the artificial watercourse runs high above the stream on its southern bank. At two points deep gorges run down to the natural stream below. At first these appear natural, but given they emanate from this channel they must be artificial. Ruinous sandstone blocks across one of these gorges suggest the remains of a regulatory overflow system. These overflow channels have been eroded to a significant width and depth, suggesting that water flowed down them for many years.

On the other side of the motorway the channel continues. It once turned south, out of the wooded region, across a field and under Raby Mere Road, to enter the lake. This section has now been in-filled. It is unknown if this supply of diverted water was only used when the mere was filled, or whether it was maintained until later in the mill's working life. The channel must certainly be at least four centuries old, but could well be significantly older. The overflow from the mere consists of two parallel sandstone culverts, of square section, which pass under the road. Evidently of great age the overflow passes around the back of the Mill House and is joined by the leat which formerly fed the mill. Together these form an almost complete circle round the Mill House. These streams both join the stream which flows through Intake Wood. The ruin of the mill still exists next to the stagnant leat which once fed it. It is on the opposite side of the road from the mere, to the west of the Mill House. The ruin is down in the valley, yet just a stone's throw from the road itself. Opposite the mill on Blakeley Road a cast iron gear is mounted on the wall. This once operated a sluice gate via a connecting rod, thus controlling the supply to the waterwheel. The connecting rod remained in place well into the 20th century.

The watermill building was evidently partially demolished many decades ago. The roof remained at the turn of the 20th century, but appears to have been dismantled soon afterwards, along with some of the stonework. Only certain walls remain and much material was obviously removed, for none of the missing stonework is anywhere to be seen. The ruin takes the form of a rectangular enclosure built from weathered red sandstone and measures approximately fifteen feet by twenty two feet. Whilst some of the walls remain almost twelve feet tall with thirteen courses of stonework, others are barely in existence. Some of the walls appear to be around three and a half feet in thickness. Next to the main building is a narrow enclosure, six feet wide, formed by one of the walls of the main mill building, and a second parallel wall. This is the wheelhouse which once housed the waterwheel. There is no sign of the roof and the ruin is fairly empty, apart from various organic detritus and some displaced blocks of sandstone. A line of holes and iron supports are built into one of the walls and a stone pillar is built into the corner between the two tallest walls; these traces doubtless show the level of the floor. The most southerly wall contains an inscribed stone on the lowest visible course. Some letters can be made out, but it is much degraded and sadly illegible.

It is most unusual that this mill has survived so close to urban development. The fact that Raby mill still exists seem remarkable. There are many references which say that it has been entirely demolished, yet it remains, seemingly forgotten and entirely undisturbed. In 1903 Mitford Abraham said "as it is beneath the level of the road and is so small, few people even notice it". Over one hundred years later this description is as true as ever.

Without a doubt, the most interesting features are the remains of the overshot waterwheel and pit wheel. These relics are probably at least one hundred and fifty years old. At the back of the wheel pit, a ceramic pipe which once fed the wheel protrudes from beneath the road. Writing in *Cheshire Life* in 1952 Marriott wrote "the wheel lingered in its ravine for many a year after the stones stopped turning". Within the former wheelhouse the two cast iron rims of the overshot wheel still exist. These would have formed the two sides of the waterwheel, the rest would likely have been built of wood; that is the spokes and wooden slats. Each half includes angled slots cast into the iron, these would have supported the wooden slats between the two halves of the wheel. Each wheel rim is made from individually cast sections joined together. One of the rims is broken just above the surface. Only part of the wheel, some eleven feet across, remains above ground level. A three and a half foot portion sticks above the ground, the rest is presumably buried. The wheel was originally twelve feet in diameter and probably some four feet wide. It seems likely that other relics could remain beneath the ground and this would be an interesting site for archaeological investigation.

Also in existence is the iron pit wheel, the large gear wheel which was directly coupled to the waterwheel via the main axle. It is within the mill building, just over the wall from the waterwheel. This large cast iron gear, with spokes, is also buried. The majority of it is below the ground. This is presumably still attached to the main iron shaft which must run through the wall of the mill below ground level. A broken fragment from a further gear protrudes from the ground nearby. There are also fragmentary remains of some broken millstones, along with the iron bands which once bound them. These are parts of French burr stones, as were commonly used for grinding wheat. The furrows cut into these fragments are plainly evident. Some fragments are around four inches thick and seem to originate from the thicker bed stone, others are only two inches in thickness and must be from the running stone.

137. Raby Mere in 2007, as seen from Blakeley Road which lies upon the mill dam. Mounted on the wall in the foreground is part of the mechanism which controlled the flow of water to the waterwheel.

138. The 17th century thatched Mill House at Raby Mere in 2010.

139. The ruined remains of the wheelhouse in 2012; the partially buried remains of the overshot waterwheel remain in place.

140. A few courses of surviving stonework at Raby mill; this wall separates the wheelhouse from the main watermill ruin.

141. The buried pit wheel can be seen within the watermill building. There is also a fragment of broken gear protruding from the earth in the foreground.

142. Looking into the ruined remains of Raby mill in 2012; most of the surviving stonework is contained in the two visible walls.

5.5 Eastham Mill

A brick built tower mill of the 18th century used to stand off the New Chester Road, to the south of Eastham village. This tower mill is shown on Burdett's map of 1777, showing it to have been of relatively early date. The first references to a windmill here appear in the late 16th century. It seems unlikely that the tower mill was built much earlier than the mid-18th century. For this reason it seems that a post mill also once stood in the area, probably on the same site. This post mill was owned by the Stanleys of Hooton Hall and operated by tenant millers.

That this site was at least 16th century in origin is shown by the 1592 rent roll of Sir Roland Stanley of Hooton, which was published in the *Cheshire Sheaf* in November 1957. This rental records that in the township of Eastham "Thomas Sparcke" paid for his dwelling "with extra for the Mille", the sum of 51s. 3d. Several generations of the Sparke family worked this mill. Thomas Sparke mentioned in the Stanley rental was the son of another Thomas who died in 1591. In his will, held at Cheshire Record Office, this older Thomas Sparke left his "dwelling house and the appurtenance the milne called Estham milne...to my son Thomas Sparke". An inventory was also made at the time of his death in 1591 and this listed that he owned "all that belonging to the milne". The younger Thomas Sparke died in 1624 and in his will he went on to leave his "wyndie corne milne" to his own son, Robert Sparke. The third generation of Sparke known to have leased Eastham mill from the Stanleys, this son worked the mill up until 1651.

143. Burdett's map shows this windmill to the south of Eastham village.

The account book of Sir Rowland Stanley of Hooton was discovered in the summer house of Hooton Hall during its demolition c.1925. This volume covers the period 1746-1751 and makes frequent references to Eastham and Storeton mills. Unfortunately it is not clear whether the mill referred to is a tower mill or post mill. No further information on when the tower mill was built can be inferred other than that it was not built within this period. It was probably constructed in either the earlier 1740s or the 1750s. The account book shows that there was a change of miller from Robert Linford to James Hough, between August and October 1747. Robert Linford was paid his last wages of £5 10s. 0d. on 31st August 1747. James Hough was still the miller in May 1751; his wages were sometimes paid in half yearly lots and sometimes quarter yearly.

The first account book entry which refers to this mill is on the 21st November 1746, when a total of £5 10s. 0d. was spent on "a millstone for Eastham Miln". Further work was carried out "putting up" a millstone at the mill in June 1748. Later that year on 21st September, £1 1s. 0d. was received for "an old millstone at Eastham Mill". General maintenance appears throughout the book; examples include – 5th December 1748 "paid James Worrall for gating Eastham Miln" £0 5s. 0d.; 24th October 1749 "paid Benjamin Tyrer for putting a sheft up at Eastham Miln" £3 6s. 4d.; 12th March 1749 "paid Thomas Walton for Iron work at Easham Miln" £0 8s. 6d. A further £0 11s. 4d. was expended on iron work in June 1751. Occasionally there is some evidence of income derived from the mill; for example on 24th October 1749, £0 1s. 0d. was received from "dressed Oates at Eastham Miln".

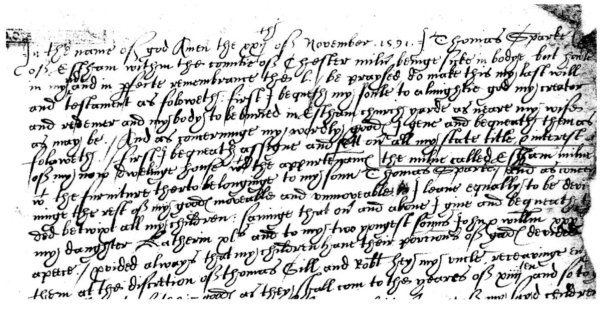

144. An extract from the will of Thomas Sparke of Eastham dated 1591. The line "the milne called Estham milne" has been surrounded by a box. (Courtesy of Cheshire Archives and Local Studies)

The later mill was a typical example of the three storey, 18th century tower mill found on Wirral. An interesting feature of this mill was an elevated pathway around the circumference of the building. This path was constructed on top of a mound built around the mill tower. It was described by Mitford Abraham as "a foot high and nine inches wide. Built against the brickwork of the mill, and securely flagged at its side by stone slabs". This raised mound must have been constructed to help the miller reach the common sails from ground level. This was necessary for the adjustment of the sailcloths.

A rumour about this mill goes that sometime during the later 19th century a storm blew down a sail. The miller removed the opposite sail and the mill then worked satisfactorily with only two sails. Unfortunately another storm c.1895 caused further damage and blew down one of the remaining sails. The miller also owned Willaston mill at this point and the sails from Eastham were used to repair Willaston mill, which had also sustained storm damage. Eastham mill never worked again. This may suggest a connection between Eastham mill and the Hale family in the 1890s; they are believed to have owned Willaston mill at this time. I cannot verify the truth of this tale; however it is certain that the mill was damaged during a storm in the mid-1890s, which ended its working life.

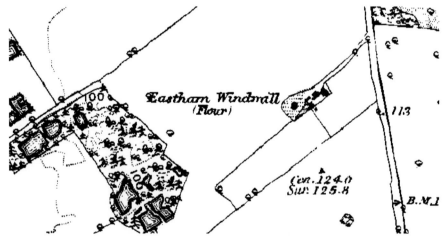

145. This Ordnance Survey map of c.1875 shows how Eastham mill was situated at the end of a track coming off the New Chester Road. (Courtesy of and Copyright Old-Maps and Ordnance Survey)

The milling machinery remained inside for some years after closure and the majority of the machinery was still there in 1903, when Mitford Abraham said "the works are still quite complete". The windshaft was of wood, with slots to admit the sails. The tithe apportionment of c.1843 shows that the mill was owned by Sir Thomas Stanley Massey Stanley. The occupier of the mill at this date was Joseph Crabb, who was the miller. The windmill remained in the hands of the Crabb family for some generations. William Crabb, son of Joseph Crabb mentioned on the tithe apportionment, was the miller in 1864, as listed in *Morris and Co.'s Directory of Cheshire* of that year. He worked the mill from at least the mid-1850s and continued to work it until his death c.1870, after which his son, also William Crabb, worked the mill into the 1890s. It was Mary Crabb who was listed as the miller here in *Slater's Directory* of 1883.

Ted Edwards moved to live in the Mill Farm alongside the mill in 1939. His parents rented the farm from building contractors, Cartwright Brothers of Little Sutton, who also owned the mill. He has told me his memories of the windmill's interior – "I well remember going inside, up ladders to the three storeys, each floor was full of timber cogs, shafts and pulleys to drive the milling done by huge grindstones of around six feet across, all in perfect condition". A range of different dates have been reported for the demolition of Eastham mill. In *Memories of Old Eastham*, Ena Stanley wrote that it was "dismantled about the 1930s much to the regret of the old villagers". *The Bebington News* of December 1979 states that – "it was demolished during the Second World War in 1942 because it was built on sand and the sand was needed". It goes on to say that "It was a great pity. It should have been preserved". The mill was actually destroyed in either November or December of 1940, as shown by the minutes of a Bromborough Society meeting around that time. The secretary of the society commented at the meeting that he had just passed the site of Eastham mill, which had very recently been demolished. Cartwright Brothers operated a sand pit next to the mill, and by 1940 they wanted to extract sand from beneath the mill itself. Ted Edwards has recalled that the mill was demolished using explosives, and several attempts were necessary, due to the thickness of the walls.

146. This photograph showing Eastham mill and the mill cottage dates to the later 1890s, probably c.1897, shortly after the mill had ceased to operate. A pair of sails remains in place, one of which is behind the tower.

147. Other than a lack of sails Eastham mill is generally well preserved in this photograph, which likely dates to c.1898. (Courtesy of Ian Boumphrey)

148. Eastham mill as photographed for James Waite's photographic survey c.1908. The windmill had not been disused for much over a decade at this point and appears fairly well preserved. (Courtesy of the Mills Archive Trust)

149. *In this second view of Eastham mill c.1908 the mound around the mill's circumference can be seen above the level of the fence. Another obvious feature are the cleats near the base of the tower. (Courtesy of the Mills Archive Trust)*

150. *This view of Eastham mill c.1900 is interesting in that it shows a slot which passed all the way through the wooden windshaft; this would once have admitted a pair of sails. (Courtesy of the Mills Archive Trust)*

151. The derelict mill at Eastham around 1938, screened by a line of poplar trees planted after it ceased to be operational. (Courtesy of Ian Boumphrey)

152. Considering it had been disused for around forty years, Eastham mill appears in a good state of preservation in this photograph of 1936. (Courtesy of Special Collections and Archives, Templeman Library, University of Kent)

153. A fairly late photograph of Eastham mill, this view must date to c.1940. The dilapidated cap may be seen from the side where a chain wheel would originally have been fitted. (Courtesy of Ian Boumphrey)

154. This photograph probably dates to 1940, and shows Eastham mill in a derelict condition shortly before it was demolished in that year. (Courtesy of the Mills Archive Trust)

Eastham mill stood along a short track, off the east side of the New Chester Road. The location is now waste ground behind a plant nursery and the original track still leads to the former mill house. This house was also once part of the Mill Farm. Reminders remain in the name of the nurseries, "Mill Nurseries" and a large house to the north is called "Mill Hey". The road name Mill Park Drive also refers to this mill. The old mill house, named "Mill Cottage", still stands by the track which once led to the mill. This house has now been rendered in pebble dash and roofed with modern tiles. It bears a datestone of 1843, but given a mill stood at this site in the 16th century, this house likely replaced a much older dwelling.

The actual site of the mill has been entirely destroyed. Sand was excavated from the land where the mill stood, possibly to a depth as great as fifty feet. This means that all evidence of the mill, including its foundations, has long since been destroyed. The sand pit was in-filled with material excavated during the construction of the uranium enrichment plant at Capenhurst, around 1945-1947. This raised the ground back up to its original level. The land where the mill stood is disused, but is accessible from the area occupied by Mill Nurseries and takes the form of a slightly raised mound. It is a large flat area which stands slightly higher than the surrounding ground. However, given this ground was formed after the mill's demolition, there is nothing to betray its former existence here.

155. These poplar trees stand in front of the site of this mill and can be seen in some of the old photographs.

156. The site of Eastham mill in 2009. This levelled area, which stands somewhat higher than the surrounding ground, covers an in-filled sand pit on the land where the mill stood.

157. The former mill house at the site of Eastham mill has a datestone of 1843.

CHAPTER 6: MILLS OF SOUTH WIRRAL

6.1 Willaston Mill

There have been windmills in Willaston for many centuries, with a succession of mills having stood in the vicinity of Mill Lane. The first mention of a mill in this area is in one of the Chester plea rolls dated 1321, as reported in the *Cheshire Sheaf* in October 1921. This concerned whether a windmill could be constructed by Oliver de Bordeaux, the lord of Willaston, the final outcome being that to build a mill would not present an "injury to the forest". Hence, permission to build a windmill was granted and this suggests that one was likely constructed here shortly afterwards. The 1321 document refers to a mill being constructed at a place named as "*Trymelowe*". In 1309 a boundary deed referred to a place known as "*Midlethrinlowe*", which was probably analogous to "*Trymelowe*". Irvine writing in the *Cheshire Sheaf* in January 1929, postulated that "*Midlethrinlowe*" must be some two hundred yards north of Willaston tower mill and Dodgson said this may be the site of the mill of 1321. Irvine commented that "*Thrinlowe*" is Middle English for a triple prehistoric burial site where "*Midlethrinlowe*" is evidently a reference to the middle mound of a group of three. It is not entirely clear how many post mills existed in Willaston, before the present mill, which is the first tower mill to have been built in the area. It has been reported that at least one mill mound from a former post mill may be found to the north of the later tower mill. A mound apparently lies near to the footpath which runs from Mill Lane to Benty Heath Lane and this may be related to the site of 1321.

An old Wirral milling family, the Lightbounds, ran the last post mill at Willaston. William Lightbound left his son, also William, the Willaston post mill along with the mill house and land in his will of 1767. This William Lightbound, who had been born in 1734, lived until 1797 at which point he left his estate, including the post mill, to his daughter Mary. Whilst he was still working the mill he was listed as "William Leghbound, miller", under Willaston, in Cowdroy's *Directory and Guide for the City and County of Chester* dated 1789. The Neston parish registers record his death and a comment alongside reads – "Not only an honest miller, but allowed to be so". Mary married another William Lightbound who it is believed was probably her cousin. It was this William Lightbound who was born in 1770 and who was likely one of the children of Samuel Lightbound of Storeton mill, who built the present tower mill around 1800. The construction was finished in 1801. He employed a millwright from Toxteth Park, Henry Gardener, and never recovered from the debts incurred during construction. Henry Gardener was apparently still owed £2288 in 1815. The Lightbounds' post mill is marked on Burdett's map of 1777, whilst the tower mill is shown on Greenwood's map of 1819. It is said that carved on to one of the tower mill's hoppers was the line – "God's providence hath been my inheritance, God bless the good old mill".

158. Burdett's map labels the Lightbounds' post mill as "Willaston Mill".

The current tower mill, which is constructed from handmade bricks, was built as a replacement for the Lightbounds' post mill. This post mill was "situated thirty yards to the west" according to Mitford Abraham. I know of no obvious evidence of its existence which can be discerned today, although traces have previously been said to exist in the mill house garden. A French burr stone was once discovered buried within this garden and was presumed to be a relic of this post mill. A fatality occurred at the post mill in 1774, when Margaret Palin was hit by the mill's sails. The brick built tower mill is five storeys tall and at some eighty feet is the tallest windmill ever to be built on the Wirral Peninsula. Williams and Crompton described it as – "possibly the earliest example in Wirral of the larger mill with taller tower and larger windows"; in fact the examples at Tranmere and Bromborough were somewhat earlier. This style was a contrast to the three storey tower mill of the earlier 18th century; a common pattern on Wirral, before the effects of industrialisation in windmill design.

The Lightbounds eventually sold the tower mill to the Rose family around 1822. In 1840 the mill was sold by the Roses to Richard Price and on his death in 1847 the ownership passed to his son Samuel. Samuel Price owned and occupied the mill on the tithe apportionment of 1848. He was also listed as a "corn dealer" in *Bagshaw's Cheshire Directory* of 1850 and as a "miller and farmer" in the 1857 *Post Office Directory of Cheshire*. The mill later passed from the hands of the Price family, to a Liverpool family, the Radfords. Samuel Radford purchased the mill in 1860 for £3500 and tried to make the mill a profitable enterprise. His hope was to create a business which could compete with the steam mills; these were beginning to spell the demise of the local mill all over the country. A single cylinder horizontal steam engine of some twenty five horsepower was installed at Willaston mill. At the same time several new pairs of stones were added to the mill, making ten pairs in total.

Six pairs of stones were driven by steam at ground level, the remaining four pairs continued to be wind powered within the tower itself. A sixty foot chimney was built alongside the mill, connected to the mill's new engine house, which adjoined the mill tower.

Mitford Abraham said that "Of all the Wirral Mills Willaston…was quite the most important as a flour mill". The mill contained five flour dressers, such that flour of a high quality could be produced on a semi-industrial scale. Production at the mill became so great that local farms could not produce enough grain to be milled there. In the 1970s Leslie Edwards recorded the valuable recollections of his father, George Edwards and also those of his grandfather, who had been employed by the Radfords from 1860, to look after their steam engine. These memories were printed in *Neston 1840-1940* and inform us that the Radfords purchased two ships. These ships were used to import grain to Birkenhead Docks from Russia. Additionally an early traction engine, the very first in the area, was purchased in the 1860s, apparently from Fowler in Leeds. This was used to transport grain from Birkenhead Docks to Willaston. If the wind conditions were suitable twenty four hour operation was employed, with several millers taking shifts. The Radfords built a bakery nearby in order to bake products using the flour they had produced. Shuttleworth, one of their bakers, became something of local legend. He carried out an advertising stunt whereby he delivered some loaves to London, made from wheat which had been growing in one of Willaston's fields earlier the same day. According to Edwards "about 50 people were employed either directly or indirectly in the running of the mill" and the Radfords were very kind employers.

Unfortunately, the Radfords efforts were not to be long-lived. By 1879, less than twenty years after buying the mill, they gave up their business. Samuel Leigh Radford, whose father had purchased the mill, could not pay the mortgage and the mortgage lenders repossessed the building. It would seem that the family underwent a financial crisis, which crippled their business. Edwards stated that this crisis was the loss of both their ships, whilst these were making the return voyage from Russia, laden with grain. However, the Burton and South Wirral Local History Society could find no other record of this loss. Other accounts have stated that the Radford family started a steam roller mill business in Liverpool and abandoned Willaston mill as unprofitable. Certainly the same family owned Albert Mill in Liverpool, from at least the 1860s. But it is believed that Samuel Radford's father already owned this steam mill, before Willaston mill was purchased. Radford's Albert Mill is mentioned in Volume 3 of Bennett and Elton's *History of Corn Milling*. This steam mill was partially converted to a roller mill in 1868, using the Buchholz partial roller system of 1862. By 1870 traditional millstones had been entirely replaced by rollers, at which point the mill was purportedly the most advanced of its kind in the country. Samuel's failure to pay his debts probably does suggest some financial tragedy, unless Willaston mill simply could not be run at a profit. The date the family ended its association with Willaston mill is generally given as 1879, but Samuel Leigh Radford was still listed there in *Slater's Directory* for 1883. The Radford family had also given up its remaining business at Albert Mill by 1903.

A family named Hawkins were the next to take over the mill. They successfully worked the mill as a flour mill, but eventually had to stop fetching grain from Birkenhead Docks, as this could not be performed profitably. It is not known if the steam mill remained in use at this point. The Hawkins ran the mill until c.1888 when they sold it to James Catto. Samuel Radford is said to have expended as much as £30,000 on the steam engine and modern equipment in the 1860s. The steam engine still existed in the early 20th century; Mitford Abraham said in 1903 that "after working a few years the new machinery had to be given up, but is still there, never to be used again". The steam engine was cut up and scrapped by James Catto during the time of the First World War, along with its boilers and other idle machinery. Latterly the Hale family, well known as Wirral millers, rented the mill from the Catto family and they ran it up until its closure.

Willaston mill turned to the less competitive business of grinding cattle feed for local farms in the late 1880s, when the Hales ran the enterprise. All flour production ceased at this point, but production of animal fodder continued into the 20th century. The mill continued to work long after many of Wirral's other windmills. It remained in use right up until early 1930. It is uncertain whether this mill was powered by wind until its last days. In a letter to the *Liverpool Daily Post* in 1936, Mitford Abraham stated that one of the mill's sails had broken whilst working in 1911, and shortly after the remaining sails were taken down. The fact that the sails were removed for a period is substantiated by photographs, which purport to show the mill with no sails around 1912 and 1914. Other sources state that the sails were repaired after storm damage in 1911. Wind power then continued until a sail was lost as the result of another gale in 1930, at which point the mill was closed. After 1930 efforts were made to power the mill via a gas engine. This had been installed in the basement some years earlier, to supplement wind power. However, running the mill entirely from the gas engine was too expensive and it became obsolete. It is assumed that wind power probably did continue until 1930, in which case this was the last working windmill on Wirral. However, Mitford Abraham's comment that the sails were removed in 1911 also seems to be correct, and it could be that the mill spent a few years out of use around this time.

The remaining sails were sawn off not long after the mill finished working. After spending some years unused the mill was auctioned in late 1933. The details of the sale indicate the scale of the premises – "the windmill, which is at present disused, has a loading door, office, granary...laundry, cottage with store...disused stable, saddle room with loft etc.". The lot was sold for £530 to a Wirral builder. Later on The Wirral Society decided to raise money to purchase the mill. They were helped by the Council for the Preservation of Rural England, who inspected the building and found it to be in reasonable condition. The Wirral Society had preservation in mind and finally bought the mill along with associated buildings in 1937; the cost was apparently £250. The Wirral Society along with the Council for the Preservation of Rural England published short articles in many local papers during 1937 and 1938. They were attempting to raise money and gain public support for the restoration of the mill. The beginning of these restoration efforts were described in the *Cheshire Observer* in April 1938. At some point in the 1930s the mill's cap was blown off revealing the machinery beneath; the society raised money for a new cap. Restoration of the mill became of little priority with the outbreak of the Second World War. During the war the mill saw use as a look out post. The home guard found that commanding views of the area could be afforded from the top.

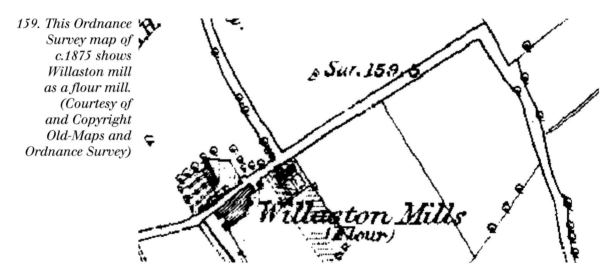

159. This Ordnance Survey map of c.1875 shows Willaston mill as a flour mill. (Courtesy of and Copyright Old-Maps and Ordnance Survey)

The Wirral Society began to find the cost of maintaining such a large building increasingly difficult. The outbuildings adjoining the mill were demolished in 1951 and at some point the mill also lost its stage. In June 1955 an article in the *Liverpool Echo* stated that demolition of the mill was imminent unless funding could be raised for repairs. By 1957 the society had put the mill up for sale, offering a decent price to anybody who would try and repair the building. Teresa Morris bought the mill in 1958 and began the difficult process of converting it into a dwelling. The conversion was a very hard job and it was two years before the Morris family could move into the mill. Such was the condition of the building, that large amounts of collapsed masonry had to be removed and all of the floors had to be replaced, since they were extremely weak.

Writing in *Cheshire Life* in 1952, Eastwood said that the mill "recently survived a well meant but abortive attempt to turn it into a private dwelling". This sounds as though a desperate attempt to preserve the mill as a house may have occurred whilst it was still owned by The Wirral Society. I do not know when the majority of machinery and original fittings were removed. They were presumably in place until some point during the 1950s, when they were dismantled and removed. The building is now grade two listed and the listing information of 1962 informs us that – "the machinery which formerly rotated the cap remains in the upper stage". The mill remained in the hands of the Morris family into the 1990s and remains a private home to this day.

160. Willaston mill is in fine working order, with a beautifully whitewashed tower, in this early 20th century photograph of Mitford Abraham's. The endless chain which was used to rotate the cap can be seen hanging down to the level of the stage. (Courtesy of The Heswall Society)

161. This watercolour was painted by Harold Hopps whilst Willaston mill was still at work in 1903. In front of the mill is the engine house, associated with the steam engine which was installed in the 1860s. (Courtesy of the Williamson Art Gallery and Museum)

163. Another view showing Willaston mill with no sails, the result of high winds in 1911. The impressive array of outbuildings adjoining the tower were demolished in 1951. (Courtesy of Ian Boumphrey)

162. This photograph shows Willaston mill with no sails in 1912. The sails had been removed, possibly following storm damage in 1911, but they were probably later reinstated, allowing the mill to operate by wind power up until 1930. (Courtesy of Ian Boumphrey)

164. Here, Willaston mill is seen from Mill Lane, probably around the mid-1930s. (Courtesy of the Mills Archive Trust)

165. The cap was blown off Willaston mill in the 1930s and had not been replaced in this 1936 photograph, which shows the mill in a slightly precarious condition. (Courtesy of Special Collections and Archives, Templeman Library, University of Kent)

166. Here, Willaston mill sports a new cap, as provided by The Wirral Society in the 1930s. The tower appears to be windowless and this photograph is likely from the 1940s. (Courtesy of Birkenhead Reference Library)

167. The partially restored mill at Willaston around the time it was converted into a dwelling in the late 1950s and early 1960s. (Courtesy of the Mills Archive Trust)

Willaston mill is the best example of a large tower mill remaining on Wirral. It is an impressive building and a fitting monument to milling on Wirral, the survival of which is extremely fortunate. It dominates the surrounding fields and appears in a good state of preservation. A series of large windows on the third floor were once doorways which opened out onto the mill's stage. Also visible near this level are the traces of the apexes of long demolished buildings which once adjoined the tower. The roofs of the mill's cellars are visible in the garden and according to Williams and Crompton these were "exposed by the demolition of the outbuildings". Also within the garden at least six millstones can be seen embedded within the ground. These are of the French burr type, used for flour production. The cast iron chain wheel which was used to rotate the cap was in situ until recent years. However, it has now been removed and rests on the ground outside. A metal cross on the end of the windshaft shows the location of the sails. The original fitting to which the sails were attached seems to have been lost during renovation. A row of sandstone cottages named "Windmill Cottages" stand adjacent to the mill. These are probably some of the buildings which were built by the Radford family and may have housed their bakery, or additional workers. There is also a large house called "The Mill House", opposite the mill on Mill Lane. This house is shown on the tithe map of c.1848 and it seems likely that it once housed the miller and their family.

168. Detail of the boat shaped cap and metal cross which shows the former position of the sails.

169. Willaston tower mill in 2009, as viewed from Mill Lane.

170. Detail of the cast iron chain wheel at Willaston mill in 2008; this feature has subsequently been removed.

6.2 Burton Mill

A windmill has stood in Burton since the early 14th century, the first known mention being a Chester county court roll dated 1315. Another early reference to a mill here is in the Palatinate of Chester Forest Proceedings for 1357. According to Dodgson in his *The Place-Names of Cheshire* this medieval manuscript mentions "*molendinum ventricitum*", that is "the windmill". A manorial account document of 1360 provides another reference to the mill in this period. In 1472 the miller was called John and paid an annual rent of £1. The common belief was once that this medieval mill stood on the hill, to the north of the village of Burton. However, another site was later shown to be the more probable location. Writing his *Notes on the Parish of Burton in Wirral*, Beazley commented with respect to field names – "Walking to the village from the railway station…the highest point of ground, is Mill Nook. The situation is a favourable one for a windmill, and there may well have been one there, though no trace of it is left". Two plots of land named "Mill Nook" lay to the south of Station Road, just east of the railway and near Peer's Wood.

These fields are marked on the tithe map of 1839. It has been suggested that the mill stood on the brow of the hill, adjacent to these fields. Further confirmation of this as the original site comes from early 14th century references to a miller at Denhall, not at Burton. According to *Burton in Wirral: A History*, a court roll of 1315 refers to the murder of "Bertram the miller of Denhall" by Stephen Golfyry. Denhall is an ancient name for the area which surrounds these fields. Another fatality is known to have occurred at this location; the Burton parish registers of 1579 record that "John Haggassman milner to Mr Massie was killed with the letbolte in Burton Mill", that is, he was struck by lightning. The composition papers of Sir William Massey Knight show that in 1646 he rented the mill and other buildings from the Bishop of Lichfield and Coventry at £20 a year. An earlier Bishop of Lichfield and Coventry was probably responsible for the construction of the original medieval windmill at Burton.

An interesting reference to the early mill is in an account of 1459, which records a millstone being conveyed from Congleton Edge. At some stage the mill was transferred to a new site, when a post mill was constructed near the end of Mill Lane, on the hilltop above Burton village. There is some uncertainty as to when a mill was first constructed on this new site. In 1609 a boundary document mentioned in *Burton in Wirral: A History* refers to "the myll hyll", and this seems to be a reference to the hill at Mill Nook, Denhall. According to 'The Parish Registers of the Parish of Burton' in the *Journal of the Chester and North Wales Archaeological and Historic Society*, the registers record that in 1629 "Burton Milne was built new by Sir William Massey Knighte about the feast of All Saints". This could well refer to substantial repairs or a rebuilding at the Station Road site. Alternatively it could be the date of abandonment of the original site and that when the new site was adopted. The year of the repairs or rebuilding coincided with the death of the miller, for the parish registers also state that "Edward Sumner milner att Burton milne dyed Suddenlie...and was buryed the xxvij° [27th] daie of March 1629". It could be that the temporary lack of a miller after Edward Sumner's death presented an opportunity to repair or rebuild the mill.

It is evident that the mill had been constructed upon the hill by the early 18th century. The first cartographic source to show the mill is Fearon and Eyes's chart of the sea coast, published in 1738. This chart clearly sketches a post mill upon the hilltop, overlooking the main village, where some cottages and a church are drawn. Burton mill appears to be erroneously marked as a watermill on Burdett's map of 1777, although the symbol is poorly engraved. This was evidently a mistake, for Burton mill was actually one of Burdett's triangulation stations, so he must have been aware what type of mill it was! Another survey which clearly indicates the location of the mill above the village is Greenwood's map of 1819.

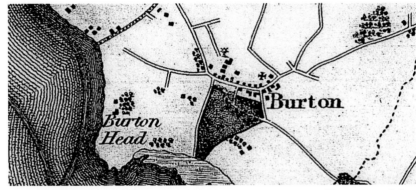

171. Greenwood's map shows Burton mill upon the hill which overlooks Burton village.

The ruinous roundhouse of a turret post mill still exists, although the remains are in very poor overall condition. The roundhouse bears a datestone, on which is inscribed "R O 1771". The initials refer to Robert Oliver, who was miller from c.1758 up until his death in 1780. His will, describing him as a miller, was proved at Chester in 1781. The date 1771 may indicate the time when a mill was first built at this second site. Alternatively it could refer to a rebuilding on this site; a mill having stood here since 1629. A datestone could have been inscribed at any point and can therefore only suggest that the building existed at that point in time. Mitford Abraham examined the main post of the mill in 1903 and commented – "several dates are carved on this shaft, one 1731". This seems to indicate that the fabric of the present ruin is probably entirely 18th century in origin, but that parts of the mill were older than the datestone on the roundhouse suggests. Even if a mill was first built here in the 17th century, that would be an early century for roundhouse use and it seems probable that nothing would remain of that structure, which would have been entirely renewed around a century later.

The accounts of Burton mill for a period in 1716 were recorded in the Burton manor court papers. John Brownsworth may have been the miller at this point. The Burton and South Wirral Local History Society reported in *Burton in Wirral: A History* that these accounts show the miller's annual salary was £8, whilst the money made from grinding the local grain came to £13 3s. 7 ½d. Taking the mill's general maintenance into account, including a new millstone at £5 19s. 6d., £2 to the millwright and 2s. 4d. to the blacksmith, the profit to the manor was only £1 7s. 1 ½d. that year. Interestingly a millstone purchased in 1472 cost only 18s., demonstrating a huge inflation in the price of a new millstone in the two hundred and forty four year period between these references.

In the 19th century this mill was rented by the Capper family, a Wirral milling family who also had a long association with Thingwall mill. John Capper posted an advertisement in the *Chester Courant* of 28th November 1809 which ran – "To be let. A capital wind-mill in a perfect state of repair, containing two pairs of stones and dressing mill, together with a good farm house…". The mill is shown on the Burton township tithe map of 1839, at which point it was owned by the Congreve family of Burton Hall. The miller at this point was Moses Smith, who was born in 1796 and who was still working the mill in 1861. He paid an annual rent of £12 to Richard Congreve. Moses Smith had been employed at Willaston mill in his youth; his name along with the date 1817 may still be seen carved into a beam in the cellar of that building. The last miller to work Burton mill may have been Thomas Joynson who was listed in *Slater's Directory* of 1869. This 18th century post mill continued to work until it was wrecked by a great gale c.1882, although some accounts alternatively place the storm in the late 1870s. It is certainly true that no miller is given at Burton in the *Post Office Directory of Cheshire* of 1878, although that does not necessarily mean the mill was then out of use. The storm caused severe damage to the building, indeed Mitford Abraham said that it had been "partially destroyed". The mill was never repaired and was abandoned at this date, never to work again.

The mill gradually became ruinous and slowly much of its fabric was removed. *Burton in Wirral: A History* states "One old resident of the village recalls that by the 1890s all available firewood had been removed from the mill, leaving the heavy beams and wheels exposed on top of the old framework. This was considered to be a danger, and so it was pulled down under the direction of Harry Parry, the Congreve family's estate bailiff". Only the most unstable material was removed; the main post was left standing upright with the crown tree (a perpendicular beam) attached at the top. The mill was in this condition for many years. Mitford Abraham stated that in 1903 – "The base of this old peg mill and some woodwork are all that remains of this once picturesque land-mark…The main shaft, seven or eight feet high with a piece of wood crossing at the top, is all that remains of the upper portion of the mill, and has some resemblance to an ancient gallows".

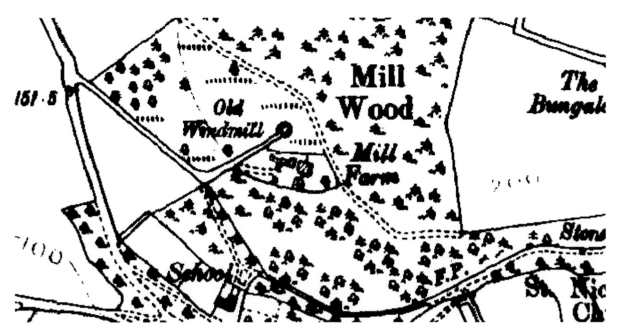

172. Burton mill was evidently disused when it was marked on this Ordnance Survey map c.1910. (Courtesy of and Copyright Old-Maps and Ordnance Survey)

At some point in the late 1920s or early 1930s the main post fell over and was left leaning against the side of the roundhouse, whilst the detached crowntree lay nearby. This was certainly the situation in 1936. The sandstone built roundhouse was virtually complete at that date and maintained its original height of approximately eight feet. Two doorways were used to gain entry to the mill's roundhouse and these remained in very good preservation well into the first half of the 20th century. When Williams and Crompton wrote of the mill in 1976 they said that – "The circular sand-stone roundhouse has partially collapsed, though the doorway…is still visible". The main post remains where it fell upon the roundhouse over eighty years ago. Williams and Crompton noted some rather interesting features of this post which were visible in the 1970s – "the main post…including the sockets for the quarter-bars and part of the bearing pin on which the mill revolved. A deep groove worn on one side of the post, immediately above the quarter-bars, shows where the lower frame of the "buck" [body] was steadied".

173. Harold Hopps's painting of Burton mill is undated and shows the mill in working order. Given Hopps was born in 1879, this post mill would have ceased to work when he was an extremely young child, and he can scarcely have known the mill in use. He is known to have based some paintings on the work of other artists and on old photographs and that might be the case here. (Courtesy of the Williamson Art Gallery and Museum)

174. The skeleton of Burton mill consisted of a motley selection of woodwork in the mid-1880s. Much of the structure had already been removed for use as firewood. (Courtesy of Birkenhead Reference Library)

175. Burton mill was in a terrible condition by the mid-1880s, even though this was not so many years after it stopped working. The mill's brake wheel can be seen silhouetted at the top of the building. (Courtesy of Ian Boumphrey)

176. The dilapidated ruins of Burton mill as photographed in the later 1880s. The precarious framework of the mill remains in place, although most machinery appears to have been removed.

177. This postcard shows the remains of Burton mill c.1908, before the collapse of the central post. The crowntree remains affixed to the top of the post. (Courtesy of Jim O'Neil)

178. The condition of Burton mill was much the same as in this photograph, from the turn of the 20th century up until the later 1920s or early 1930s, when the main post collapsed. (Courtesy of Ian Boumphrey)

179. The stonework of Burton mill's roundhouse remained in a good condition in 1936. One of the holes built to admit the end of a crosstree may be seen. (Courtesy of Special Collections and Archives, Templeman Library, University of Kent)

180. An interesting 1930s view; the main post of Burton mill may be seen leaning on the side of the roundhouse. In front of the roundhouse the crowntree assembly lies in disarray. (Courtesy of Birkenhead Reference Library)

The mill's datestone remains in place, one course from the top of the roundhouse, but is entirely covered by dense ivy. In 1903 Mitford Abraham said "There are two doorways into the basement, one at the north side, and the other at the south side; near the latter, low down by the ground, is a stone with R O 1771 inscribed on it". However, the book *Burton in Wirral: A History* says "In February 1981 the date-stone...was still in position one course below the top of the drum to the left of the southern doorway at a height of some 7 feet above the ground". The ruin became grade two listed in 1962, at this point it was recorded that "only eight courses now remain of the original structure". Presently, the ruin only contains seven courses of stonework at the highest extent, but most of the structure is much lower. It appears that the datestone may have been moved into the more noticeable position, where it remains to this day, at some point in the 20th century. The condition of the ruin has deteriorated severely in the last few decades. The ravages of time and mindless vandalism certainly appear to have taken their toll on the structure. Today no part of the ruin has a height of much more than some six and a half feet. There is evidence that the ruin was well maintained in the past. However, the structure is now a sad sight and is in sore need of restoration, before being lost completely. At the turn of the 21st century the ruin was free of ivy, but the last fifteen years have seen ivy grow unrestrained, and this can only weaken the final remains of this once sturdy structure.

181. The degraded remnants of Burton mill's roundhouse as they appeared in late 2000, before being enveloped by ivy in the years that followed. (Courtesy of Jim O'Neil)

182. Detail of the datestone inscribed "R O 1771", as photographed at Burton mill in November 2000. (Courtesy of Jim O'Neil)

The ruins of Burton mill are visible to the left of a path, which leads into the National Trust owned Burton Mill Wood, from the end of Mill Lane. The structure is within the garden of a house called "Mill Hey" and consists of the circular roundhouse, approximately eighteen feet across at the base. Much of the roundhouse has been destroyed and the remaining wall varies between six and a half and three feet in height. Some of the wall has evidently collapsed and the interior of the roundhouse is filled with a sad assortment of sandstone rubble. Although impressive I maintain that basic maintenance is needed, or this important relic of our past will be lost.

Several points of interest may be revealed by close examination of the ruin. Around the circumference of the roundhouse, at ground level, there are four rectangular holes built into the wall. These are spaced at ninety degree intervals and once accepted the wooden crosstrees, an important part of a post mill's substructure, used to support the central post. The roundhouse was probably built around the crosstrees after the rest of the mill had already been constructed. A section of the roundhouse has completely vanished on the southern side. One side of the southern doorway remains, at the point where the ruin retains a height of seven courses. Total collapse of the structure has led to the loss of the other side of this doorway. The other feature of interest is the mill's main post, some thirteen feet long. This has been leaning on the side of the roundhouse since it fell down in the late 1920s or early 1930s. If the date which Mitford Abraham saw carved into it a century ago is reliable, it is probably around three centuries since this was formed from the trunk of a tree.

Also in existence is the old miller's house, called "Mill Cottage", which stands in Mill Lane and has been extended several times. The original cottage was a long rectangular building of local sandstone. This bore a datestone of 1774, along with the initials of Robert and Mary Oliver. By the first half of the 19th century a perpendicular addition had been attached to the original building. This extension appears to be marked on Bryant's map of 1831. A former stable block, now another residence, exists next to the old mill cottage; this building is shown on Bryant's map and on the tithe map of 1839. The first modern extension is upon the frontage of the original cottage. It is sandstone built and dates to the 1920s. The original datestone was relocated when this extension was built. The most modern extension is from the 1960s and is brick built. Within the house, behind the 1920s extension, the original doorway of the 1770s exists and is formed from roughly hewn sandstone pillars.

183. The Mill Cottage at Burton, as viewed from its grounds in 2009.

184. The gable end of the former stable block adjacent to Mill Cottage. In the background is an old sandstone pig sty.

6.3 Little Stanney Mill

A watermill was recorded in Little Stanney township before 1184, when it was mentioned in the Chartulary of St. Werburgh's Abbey as "*molendinum de Staneya*". A translation of the Latin chartulary was published by the Chetham Society in two parts; this charter is in Part 2 published in 1923. The transaction involved Humphrey de Bunbury Knight who gave various land, along with the mill of Stanney, to the monks of St. Werburgh's, in exchange for Peckforton and four oxgangs in Little Stanney. The document was assigned a date by the fact that it involved William Patrick of Malpas, who died in 1184. According to Dodgson's *The Place-Names of Cheshire*, another early reference to a mill in this township is in the Coucher Book of Whalley Abbey, which refers to Flyndal mill in 1279 as "*molendinum de Flyndal*". This mill was probably related to Flyndale, an ancient watercourse and one of the township boundaries, separating Little Stanney and Great Stanney. These two references could be related to the same site, which is undoubtedly amongst the oldest in this book.

However, in the 12th century there may have been a second watermill in this vicinity, for separate mills seem to have coexisted in both Little Stanney and Great Stanney townships. The charter which gave Little Stanney mill to the monks of St. Werburgh's has already been mentioned. A second charter, listed in Part 1 of the Chetham Society's *The Chartulary or Register of The Abbey of St. Werburgh, Chester*, involved John Constable of Chester who "gave to the abbey the mill of (Great) Stanney". This charter was dated in the range 1163-1190. When Stanlow Abbey was founded in 1178 the township of Great Stanney was granted to it, by the same John Constable who gave St Werburgh's Great Stanney mill. The charter likely predates 1178 since it seems unlikely St. Werburgh's Abbey would be given Great Stanney mill after Stanlow Abbey had been granted that township. Land disputes in Stanney are known to have taken place between the monks of the two abbeys. Great Stanney mill and Flyndal mill could be analogous to one another. The monks of Stanlow left their abbey and moved to Whalley Abbey in 1296. This may have led to charters from Stanlow being transferred to the Coucher Book of that abbey. The reference to Flyndal mill in the Coucher Book of Whalley Abbey is perhaps most likely a reference to Great Stanney mill, given Stanlow Abbey and later Whalley Abbey's ownership of that township.

The Bunbury family, of Stanney Hall, had occupied land in Little Stanney from the 12th century. Having handed possession of the watermill there to St. Werburgh's Abbey before 1184, it later came back into their ownership. Henry Bunbury died in 1597 and his inquisition post mortem, printed in Ormerod's *History* of Cheshire, lists that he "held the manor and water-mill of Little Stanney". The mill passed to Thomas Bunbury after Henry Bunbury's death. He certainly held the mill in 1600; at this date an agreement was negotiated between Thomas Bunbury and people including William Aldersey, who spoke on behalf of residents in Picton, Stoke and Wervin townships. The agreement, preserved at Cheshire Record Office, involved maintenance of a "frame and two gates", on the watercourse before Little Stanney mill. Measures were taken to avoid flooding nearby land.

The last mill stood outside the village of Little Stanney to the north east, but it is difficult to say how this corresponded to any ancient site. It was worked by a small brook, which joins the River Gowy some way south of Stanlow Point. The River Gowy forms the boundary of the Hundred of Wirral and this mill stood only just within that area. According to Irvine the mill remained in the hands of the Bunbury family until the mid-19th century, when it passed to the Dean and Canons of Chester, along with the rest of the Stanney and Stoke estate. The final mill to stand here was powered by an undershot waterwheel, in a similar manner to Bromborough watermill. This mill was a brick built building, three storeys high and containing four pairs of millstones. In Mitford Abraham's opinion the mill was not "much more than one hundred years old" (in 1903). Despite this he went on to remark – "The base and foundations are of stone, and as in one or two places alterations appear to have taken place, it is most likely that the present building succeeded a much older one".

Mitford Abraham's deduction would seem to be correct as far as age is concerned. There is an advertisement for this mill in the *Chester Courant* of 25th December 1827; this runs – "To be let, a newly erected water corn mill situated in the township of Little Stanney in the Hundred of Wirral. It contains three pairs of French Stones and one pair of Grey Stones with dressing and smithing machines together with a dwelling house and outbuildings". Certainly this seems to imply that the mill had only just been built. We can assume that this was a substantial rebuilding, on a considerably older site, since the mill is shown at this site on Burdett's map of 1777 and existed at this location from at least that date. Bryant's map of 1831 marks the watermill and labels the watercourse south of the mill as "River Twine". This is the only known instance of this river name.

Whether the location on Burdett's map was the site of the ancient watermill associated with St. Werburgh's Abbey remains uncertain. An inquisition post mortem dated 1636, which was an enquiry into the death of Sir Henry Bunbury Knight, was published in *Cheshire Inquisitions Post Mortem: Stuart Period 1603-1660*. This inquisition states that "the said Sir Henry...was seised...of the manor & capital messuage of Little Stanney & of 2 water grain mills...& 100 acres of moor in Little Stanney". This reference seems unambiguous in the assertion that there were two watermills in Little Stanney at this time. Further evidence for two mills comes from the details of Sir Henry Bunbury's estate around the time of the Civil War. His estate was said to include two watermills in Stanney, and before he was held prisoner early in 1645, these had been valued at £20 per annum. However, a second mill is not mentioned in the inquisition dated 1597, relating to the death of another Henry

Bunbury. The monastic mill could have stood at a site which continued to be occupied by a mill owned by the Bunbury family into the 17th century. Maybe the Bunburys later built a second mill at a different site in the township between 1597 and 1636. It could be that this 17th century mill occupied the later site, but that 1636 marked a transient period where both mills remained in use. Such a rebuilding does not even require a second site. A new mill could have been constructed alongside an older mill, both in the vicinity of the ancient monastic site, and for a time in the early 17th century both mills may have been used simultaneously. Alternatively, documents of this period are sometimes known to refer to multiple mills, when they are actually only listing several pairs of millstones within the same building. It cannot be ignored that this could be the case here.

The tithe map of Little Stanney township from c.1845 marks the watermill. The owner of the mill at this point was Sir Henry Edward Bunbury and the miller was Rupert Fernyhough. The Fernyhoughs were an old Cheshire milling family. In the mid-19th century they also ran Trafford mill which was on the River Gowy, in Mickle Trafford township. The tithe map demonstrates the nature of the leat which fed the mill. Interestingly there was never any sizeable mill pool at this site. This meant that there was never a large reserve of water with which to power the mill. The watercourse to the south of the mill was altered such that it formed a long leat, which took the form of two parallel watercourses, with a strip of land in between them. This would have allowed for better regulation of flow to the undershot wheel. Old photographs suggest that the western branch of the stream bypassed the mill, whilst the eastern branch turned the waterwheel. The tithe map marks various buildings at the end of a trackway which terminated when it reached the mill brook. One of these buildings was built over the stream itself and this was presumably the watermill building.

185. The nature of the leat south of this mill is shown on the tithe map. Little Stanney mill must have been the rectangular building directly above the watercourse. (Courtesy of Cheshire Archives and Local Studies)

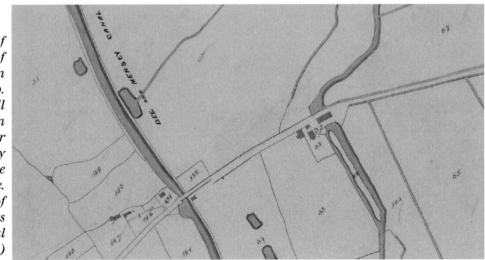

Mitford Abraham emphasised that "This mill was one of the most important in Wirral". The 1827 advertisement already mentioned also highlights the transport connections available at this mill, for it was "within about a hundred yards of the Ellesmere Canal which affords ready communication with Liverpool and Manchester". Although a major concern in its heyday, the mill had stopped producing flour by the later 1880s. The mill had some equipment which was superior to that of other local mills, such as a flour dresser, and Mitford Abraham said that it was "still provided with the silk dresser for sifting the flour after it has gone through the stones. This is a good instance of a country mill, combining the use of stones with the silk dresser, endeavouring to compete with the modern roller mill". All the same, this mill could not provide serious competition to the steam roller mill and flour production ceased. Following the discontinuation of flour, the mill concentrated on producing animal fodder; this was the final fate of many a country mill.

In 1883 the miller at Litte Stanney mill was Stephen Davies Junior, who was recorded in *Slater's Directory*. The mill ceased to function in the early 20th century; it had definitely closed by the outbreak of the First World War. In *Kelly's Directory* for Cheshire of 1906, there is a Walter Dodd recorded to be the miller at Little Stanney. He was probably the last miller, for there is no miller shown at Little Stanney in the directory of 1910. It seems likely that the mill ceased to work between these dates. The site of the mill was visited by Graham Connah in 1950. An account of the visit is included in Volume 2 of his journal. The mill had been demolished by this date and Connah states – "All this area is now under the "Shell" petroleum company, and it is they, poor fools, who for no conspicuous reason, have (some years back) pulled down this water mill." From this we can infer that the mill was probably demolished in the latter half of the 1940s.

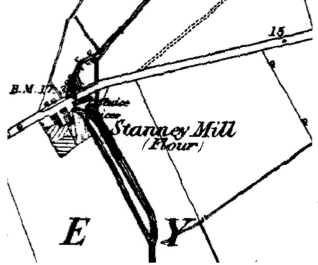

186. Little Stanney mill was shown as milling flour on this Ordnance Survey map c.1875. A pair of sluice gates is marked on the leat south of the mill. (Courtesy of and Copyright Old-Maps and Ordnance Survey)

The mill's leat was still an obvious feature in 1950. Connah noticed sections of concrete, with slots for a sluice gate, on either side of the eastern channel. He sketched the site of the mill on the western bank of the westerly channel. On the tithe map there is only a single bridge over the leat. Later Ordnance Survey maps show the two channels splitting at some forty five degrees to one another and each flows under the road separately, by means of two bridges. In 1950 Connah noted that the bridge over the western channel was based on a stone foundation, suggesting it was of some age. The eastern bridge had foundations of more modern brickwork.

187. The three storey, 19th century watermill at Little Stanney as seen c.1903. This photograph appears to be looking upstream, having been taken to the north of the lane on which Little Stanney mill was situated. (Courtesy of the Mills Archive Trust)

188. Mitford Abraham used this photograph of Little Stanney mill to illustrate his 'The Old Flour Mills of Wirral' in 1903. This view is looking downstream along the western branch of the mill brook. (Courtesy of the Mills Archive Trust)

189. Little Stanney mill as captured by James Waite for his photographic survey c.1908, around the time this mill stopped operating. A man, who could have been the miller, may be seen in front of the building. (Courtesy of Birkenhead Reference Library)

The memory of this mill lives on in the road names Stanney Mill Road and Stanney Mill Lane. There is also the Stanney Mill Industrial Estate and the watercourse which powered the mill retains the name "Mill Brook" on Ordnance Survey maps. Apart from these reminders, there is nothing to be seen. Increased industrial development in the area has enveloped the site of the mill. The track which led to the mill is now Stanney Mill Lane, but this has entirely disappeared at the point where it crossed the mill brook. The site is not even accessible for public examination, as it is now inside a private industrial complex.

6.4 Great Saughall or the Gibbet Mill

A three storey brick built tower mill of 18th century origin still stands in Great Saughall township. This mill is situated on Parkgate Road, some way south of Woodbank Lane. In its past the mill has earned a more interesting name than that denoted by its geographical location. It is commonly referred to as the Gibbet mill.

In 1750 it is said that there were three Irish farm labourers, making their way home after a summer's work. The men quarrelled over their earnings and this led to one man being killed and robbed by the other two. They took his earnings, along with any other possessions of value, before hiding his body at a spot not far from where the mill now stands. Not content with the money gained from the murder of their companion, the murderers went on to commit another crime at a local public house. Some say that the men went to the Greyhound Inn in Shotwick, where they attempted to rob the savings of the landlady. It has alternatively been claimed that they were the cause of some further violence at the Greyhound Inn. Other accounts say that they never went to the Greyhound at all, but to the Swinging Gate in Saughall, where they went on to commit further crimes.

Either way, their later crimes, whatever they were, did not go unnoticed. Alarms were raised over their actions and a capture was attempted. The men tried to flee, however they were caught and it was later discovered that they had killed their companion. They were conveyed to Chester where they were tried and found guilty of murder, for which they were hanged. Another variation of this tale is that there were originally four Irish harvesters, rather than three. At the assizes in Chester, one of the remaining three labourers gave evidence against his two companions, thus escaping punishment himself. Either way, having been executed the bodies of two murderers were taken back to the scene of their initial crime and gibbeted from an old ash tree on Parkgate Road. This tree is said to have stood just north of the mill and via this association, the mill earned its grisly name.

One of the versions of this old story undoubtedly has a large element of truth, for the execution is reported in the *Chester Courant* of 25th September 1750. It was reported that – "Last Saturday about three o'clock in the afternoon, Garrat Delany, and Edward Murray were, pursuant to their sentence at the last Assizes, for the murder of Brian Molloy, executed at Boughton, near this City. They behaved with great decency, acknowledged the fact, and the justness of their sentence, and were both very pertinent. They were that evening hung up in irons near the Two Mills on the Heath, in the Road to Parkgate". The reference to Two Mills is not relevant to this mill, but will be discussed in Appendix A.

Since the murder occurred in 1750 it is debatable whether this tower mill had actually been built at that point. In an intriguing deviation from the normal, Burdett's map of 1777 describes the building as "A new Mill". This seems to suggest that the mill was built during the early 1770s, for Burdett's map was surveyed from 1772-1774, and why else would the mill have been marked in this way? In their introduction to a facsimile reprint of Burdett's map, Harley and Laxton mention that Great Saughall mill was advertised in the *Chester Chronicle* of 4th April 1777 as "a new-erected brick wind-mill". However, the mill was probably already a few years old when advertised. Burdett's map was published on 1st January 1777, but Burdett had left Liverpool in 1774, by which point the plates for the map were likely to have been already engraved. Assuming the final surveying took place before Burdett had left the area, a construction date in the early 1770s is some decades after the date of the murder. It seems probable that following its construction, the mill became associated with the events which had occurred nearby some years earlier. The mill has been marked as "Gibbet Mill" on maps for many years, for example Bryant's map of 1831 clearly marks it as such.

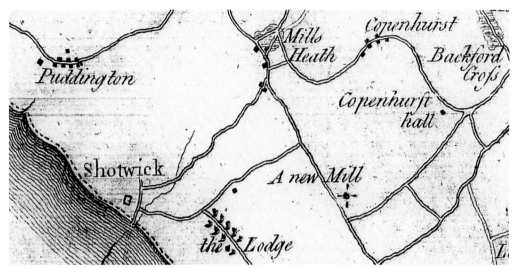

190. Intriguingly Burdett described the Gibbet mill as "A new Mill" on his survey.

The mill is shown on the tithe map for Great Saughall township of c.1849. The owner at this time was Reverend Richard Richardson of Capenhurst Hall, as revealed by the tithe apportionment. It was he who founded, and instigated the construction of, the Holy Trinity church at Capenhurst in the 1850s. The occupier at this date was James Ellison, who was also listed as a corn miller at "Saughall Mills" in *Bagshaw's Cheshire Directory* of 1850. He lived in the mill house which stands just south of the mill itself. There was a change of miller some years after the tithe map was produced, for it was Thomas William who was recorded as a "miller & farmer" in the *Post Office Directory of Cheshire* for 1857. By 1883 the miller was Ralph Davies, who has an entry in *Slater's Directory* of that year. The Carter family were the last millers to work this mill. William Carter is listed here in *Kelly's Directory* for 1902 and also in 1906. Interestingly both directories list him as a miller using both "wind & steam", although no information has been found concerning the use of steam at the Gibbet mill, and Mitford Abraham did not mention it being used in 1903.

Along with Willaston mill, this was the only one of Wirral's windmills to work well into the 20th century. Mitford Abraham said in 1903 that the mill had "lately been considerably modernised"; this must have occurred around the turn of the 20th century. These modern additions included a fantail. Although these devices were commonplace in some parts of the country, this seems to be the only one of Wirral's windmills to have been fitted with one. Most of the peninsula's mills used the antiquated system of turning the cap using a hand operated chain up until closure. A pair of spring sails was also fitted at the same time. Only two of these spring sails were used, the remaining pair being the older common type.

Spring sails did not generate as much power as the equivalent common sails and it was common practice to fit a pair of each. This gave the miller the best of both worlds. Mitford Abraham noted that "It is rather strange to see this pair of arms working along with the old pair requiring sails"; by that he meant the other pair needed sailcloths, pieces of cotton which covered the wooden frames, so they would catch the wind.

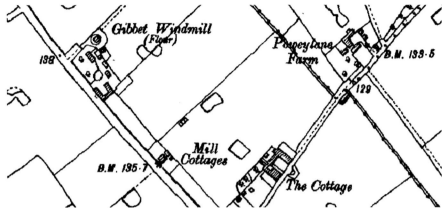

191. On this Ordnance Survey map of c.1910 the Gibbet mill was marked as producing flour, at a time when most of Wirral's windmills had already ceased to operate. (Courtesy of and Copyright Old-Maps and Ordnance Survey)

This mill hung on until Wirral's milling era was virtually over, working until 1926, whilst Willaston lingered on until 1930. So the Gibbet mill was one of the last of Wirral's many windmills to function in a traditional manner. In common with other local mills, this mill was probably used for animal feed production towards the end of its life. It seems likely that this windmill was the last to produce flour on Wirral. Willaston mill had ceased flour production by 1885. This mill with its modernised machinery continued producing flour somewhat longer, probably into the 20th century. After closure the mill was regrettably allowed to fall into disrepair.

Eastwood writing for *Cheshire Life* in 1952 said "In the mill house lives Mr. Carter, grandson of a miller who knew the Gibbet Mill in its heyday. His sister told me that the mill was scheduled for repair just before the war, but of course the plans fell through when war broke out". This seems remarkable, for given this must be a reference to the Second World War, it barely seems plausible that consideration had been given to working this mill as a profitable business in the 1940s. One would have thought that economic hardship, due to the mill losing money, must have led to its closure more than a decade earlier. Even the mighty Willaston mill had ceased to function by wind power in 1930; it remains as a testament to the fact that windmills in the area were no longer in any way economical to operate.

This mill remained in a reasonable condition for some years after closure. Later on it rapidly fell into an increasingly ruinous state. The photographic record shows that the mill was in good condition, with all sails remaining, in 1934. Later in the 1930s one of the sails fell off, after which dereliction was ensured. By the mid-1950s the cap had been blown off, whilst the remaining three sails appeared worn and skeletal. The windshaft was exposed and the brake wheel silhouetted against the sky. Eastwood visited the mill in the late 1940s and commented on its longevity in *Cheshire Life* in 1952 – "as I climbed cautiously up the steps inside and trod over the rotting floors below the vast machinery, I found abundant evidence of this [the fact the mill worked until 1926] in the great amounts of chaff lying everywhere. It is a pleasant thought to realise this windmill was still working in one's own lifetime; but the mill itself has fallen into a sad state of disrepair". Later in the 1950s, the floors of the mill collapsed. Norman Ellison noted this when he visited the mill in 1952. Writing in *Cheshire Life* in 1975 he commented – "in 1952 it was in such a ruinous state that entrance was impossible. The interior floors and machinery had collapsed into a tangled mass".

192. c.1895 prior to its modernisation the Gibbet mill had four common sails and a cap rotated by a chain wheel, the endless chain from which can be seen behind the mill. (Courtesy of the Mills Archive Trust)

193. c.1905 after being modernised the Gibbet mill sported two common sails and two spring sails, whilst the cap was turned by means of a fantail. (Courtesy of the Mills Archive Trust)

194. This photograph of Mitford Abraham's dates to c.1903 and shows the 18th century mill house alongside the Gibbet mill. (Courtesy of the Mills Archive Trust)

195. The Gibbet mill had evidently fallen out of use when this photograph was taken, for some of the slats are missing from the spring sails. This view likely dates from the early 1930s. (Courtesy of Ian Boumphrey)

196. The sails were never removed from the Gibbet mill after closure and by the late 1930s both types of sail were in a very poor condition. (Courtesy of the Mills Archive Trust)

*197. The Gibbet mill
retained three skeletal
sails throughout
the 1950s. This
photograph probably
dates to the early
1950s when parts of
the cap still remained
in place. (Courtesy of
Birkenhead Reference
Library)*

*198. The Gibbet
mill as it
appeared from
fields bordering
Parkgate Road in
the 1960s, less than
a decade before
it was converted
to residential use.
(Courtesy of the
Mills Archive
Trust)*

The derelict mill was eventually converted into a family home around 1971, with some preliminary work in the late 1960s. The conversion, carried out by J. D. Parker, included the addition of a single storey extension which adjoins the mill on the southern side. Various openings were also created, for the insertion of new windows. This conversion ensured the mill's long term preservation; however, as is usually the case, it was probably at this point that much of the remaining machinery disappeared. The mill was provided with a replica set of sails by a millwright who was employed in the conversion called Derek Ogden. These were designed to appear like the sails used in the mill's later years; there is a pair of spring sails and a pair of common sails. The main difference is that these replicas are shorter than the originals. Since the mill was without a stage, the original sails came very close to the ground so that the sailcloths could be adjusted.

This mill has been a grade two listed building since 1952. The listing description dating from 1985 informs us that inside the mill a "Massive partly shaped post runs up through the tower. Loft contains a large cast-iron shaft on square wooden framework". These are presumably the only original features which remain in place. The cast iron shaft must be the windshaft to which the sails were attached and this evidently remained in place when conversion occurred. It is possible that the brake wheel is also still in situ upon the shaft. This windmill appears to be in very good condition and is another fortunate survivor. It is Wirral's only windmill other than Bidston mill to carry a replica set of sails. The mill house also exists to this day and appears in excellent repair; Mitford Abraham said it was "of the same age as the mill". The Gibbet windmill, along with the mill house next door, provides a very good example of an 18th century tower mill and miller's residence.

199. The Gibbet mill at Great Saughall, as seen from the footpath to Capenhurst in 2008.

200. This view of the Gibbet mill shows the replica pairs of common sails and spring sails which have been fitted.

201. The 18th century mill house which stands next to the mill, as seen in 2011. The sails of the mill can be seen to the left of the house.

PART 3: MILLS DISUSED PRIOR TO BURDETT'S 1772-1774 CHESHIRE SURVEY

This book aims to record, as far as possible, all of the windmills and watermills to have existed within the boundaries of the Hundred of Wirral. Thus far however, it has only covered the mills which existed up to c.1774, and appeared on Peter Burdett's map published in 1777. There are already multiple instances where mills which ceased to work before Burdett's survey have been mentioned, but only when these earlier mills were replaced by a later structure. Some of Wirral's mills had stopped working before Burdett surveyed Cheshire, never to be replaced by a later mill. Part 3 of this book aims to describe those early mills, for which primary documents are known to support their existence. When attempting to identify sites, field name evidence is relied upon in many instances, often from tithe maps and sometimes from older estate maps. An examination of further field names, at sites where no known documentation survives, is provided in the second part of Chapter 9, within Part 4. To qualify for a section in Part 3 a possible location has been suggested for each site. Some further primary references are known for additional mills, but it was not possible to deduce where within their townships these mills may have stood. Those mills where no site could be proposed have also been placed within Part 4, Chapter 9.

Some field names are likely to commemorate sites of great antiquity, although Bott proposed in his 'Cornmill Sites in Cheshire 1066-1850' that – "It is suggested that field name sites - particularly those of windmills - were most likely to have been occupied by cornmills during the C17 and/or first half of the C18". Some of these structures vanished so long ago, that in many cases little detail is known about them. It is easy to be over-dogmatic with field names, and in his account Bott assigns fields which are very close to each other, as containing multiple sites, in a fairly generous manner. He felt that a quarter of a mile was "probably far enough to indicate a separate windmill". I have treated field names a little more sceptically and their use certainly requires caution. Some of Wirral's mills certainly appear to have given rise to mill related field names over a quarter of a mile from their sites. Many names undoubtedly show windmill or watermill sites, but not necessarily conclusively. In situations where there is no physical reference to a mill, field names do little more than provide a basis for speculation, where the existence of a mill might be impossible to prove.

Bott considered that the value and permanent nature of watermills in Cheshire, was likely to lead to their mention in such documents as land charters and inquisitions post mortem, yet he admitted that – "there is no means of knowing the proportion of sites for which such papers survive". However, he considered that – "if the extent of our knowledge on watermill sites is uncertain, the case is worse with windmills. Some of them were relatively small and lightweight. Timber-built, they were easy to erect and dismantle and their use on any one site might be short, they could be looked upon as agricultural equipment rather than permanent buildings". This is an interesting consideration, which is easily overlooked considering the permanent nature of the 18th century tower mill and also of later post mills. Paterson in his survey of 'The Development of Post Mills in the NW' written for the North West Mills Group mentions several Lancashire post mills which were dismantled and reconstructed elsewhere, sometimes as late as the early 19th century. This practice seems to have been fairly common at many localities throughout the country. No records are known concerning Wirral's post mills being moved in such a manner. However, the dearth of information on the early mills means that this was not necessarily an unknown occurrence. It may be that it was only some centuries after their initial introduction that the post mills built on Wirral took on a more permanent role.

Constructional details were not recorded for the early post mills. Although relatable to the more substantial turret post mills, the earliest post mills would likely have been very lightly constructed. These insubstantial structures would have been of the tripod and sunk types described in the Introduction and other variants of these types could also have existed. It has been suggested by Paterson that the woodwork which supported the central post underwent an evolution, which has not been fully pieced together, due to the incomplete archaeological record. For many centuries post mills were based on wood and earthworks. Stone and brick built roundhouses did not feature until much later and were probably absent from most post mills described in this section. Some of the early windmills listed in Part 3 were undoubtedly fairly short-lived.

Bott believed that a possible lack of early medieval mills, prior to the 1280s, in some areas of Cheshire including Wirral, was due to their preservation as game forests, with forest laws limiting agriculture. Yet he considered that "Wirral Forest is the exception…it was relatively well populated rather than purely for the preservation of game; and the growth of mills suggest that restrictions were relaxed there relatively early." Forest regulations were a Norman concept and some forest restrictions may have been enforced on Wirral under a century after the Conquest. Such laws restricted building new structures, including the construction of windmills, the erection of which may have incurred large fines. Forest regulations were very oppressive and were a great source of resentment to much of Wirral's population. It has traditionally been suggested that the afforestation of Wirral was instigated by Randle de Meschines, the 3rd Earl of Chester, sometime before his death in 1129. However, Volume 2 of *The Victoria County History of the County of Chester* suggests that a charter of the 6th Earl of Chester, Ranulf de Blondeville, dated 1194-1208, is the first true evidence of Wirral being designated as a forest for game preservation. The Palatinate of Chester Forest Proceedings are a series of 13th and 14th century records relating to the Cheshire forests. These are preserved in The National Archives (reference: CHES 33), and references to them are taken from Dodgson. They are referred to multiple times in Part 3, for they provide valuable references to some of the little known mills covered in this section.

In 'The Disafforestation of Wirral' Stewart-Brown mentions that in 1347, many of those who inhabited both Wirral and Delamere forests were taken to court, for offences by which they had broken forest laws. This court was known as an eyre and offences committed included "Houses and mills built without licence". It was ordered that these must be destroyed. This suggests that illegal windmills, constructed whilst Wirral was governed by forest restrictions, might have existed only for very brief periods, leaving few traces. It has not been discovered specifically where any illicit windmills stood in Wirral or Delamere forests, but there could well have been sites on Wirral. In 1357 a fine of £1000 was levied on the forest of Wirral, the results of a second forest eyre, which decreed Wirral's residents had again broken forest laws.

The eyre of 1347 was the first of its kind to be held in Cheshire, and it is not clear how the building of new mills was regarded before that time. The aim of the eyre was purely to raise money through fines, a source of revenue being required by Edward the Black Prince, who was Earl of Chester. The eyre of 1347 was financially unsuccessful, but subsequently forest laws were enforced more rigorously, meaning the eyre of 1357 was more prosperous. The Record Society of Lancashire and Cheshire published a transcription of *Accounts of the Chamberlains and other Officers of The County of Chester 1301-1360*. These accounts record that for the year 1358-1359, £175 11s. 1d. was received from the community of "the Forest of Wyrhale"; this being part of their £1000 fine, which was to be paid over five years. There follows a list of the offences for which the fine had been imposed including – "sowing their lands with corn, waste and destruction of woods, building of houses and wind-mills, making bricks, and for trespass of vert and venison". Hence, some primitive and unlicensed windmills certainly existed in the Forest of Wirral at the time of the 1357 eyre.

The records of the 1357 eyre are in The National Archives (reference: CHES 33/6). They have recently been published as *Cheshire Forest Eyre Roll 1357 - Part One: The Forest of Wirral* by The Record Society of Lancashire and Cheshire. There are references within the eyre to mills which were said to be newly built in 1357. An approximate date of construction is given for these mills, and many of these dates appear to be rounded to the nearest ten years. Hence there are mills which were said to have been built in 1317, 1327 and 1337, for the period covered by the eyre extended back a number of decades. Windmills constructed during this period were generally said to be "to the harm of the beasts", the beasts being the deer. New buildings were thought to reduce the deer's freedom to roam and were thus liable for a fine. Mills described as newly built in 1357, but actually built decades before, were probably those which had been constructed illegally, but for which a fine had not been paid. All of the windmills which had been built during the period of the eyre were subject to a fine of 40s. The windmills were also valued at half a mark (6s. 8d.) per year, and this was added to the fine for every year a mill had been in existence.

The 1357 eyre roll also frequently states that the windmills mentioned were "to be forfeited and destroyed", and other similar comments. Dr. Paul Booth has suggested to me that although documents relating to the 1347 and 1357 eyres emphasise that unauthorised windmills should have been pulled down, it is highly probable that this did not happen. Instead, the landowners who had constructed mills without permission would have been willing to pay a fine, to prevent demolition. This would have satisfied the Black Prince's government, whose chief interest lay in using the forest restrictions to raise money.

Wirral was disafforested in a charter granted by Edward III in 1376, the result of a deathbed request of his son the Black Prince. A transcription of the charter printed by Booth in 'The Last Week of the Life of Edward the Black Prince' states that "the said place called Wirral, and everything contained within its bounds, shall be entirely disafforested for ever". William Stanley, Wirral's master forester, disputed the disafforestation and Edward III's charter was not confirmed by parliament before his death. Some aspects of forest law seem to have been enforced for almost a decade more, up until the mid-1380s. However, if the demolition of Wirral's illegal mills was not enforced, fines being paid instead to avoid demolition, Wirral's exemption from forest law may have had no significant effect on the building of new mills. It is evident from the details of the 1357 eyre that illicit windmills were not necessarily short-lived, but were often allowed to exist for decades, despite being officially prohibited.

Some of the mills in this section are subject to passing reference in other published works, whilst many others have never been described before. The mills in Part 2 still exist or existed into the relatively recent past, a few centuries ago. Some of the mills in Part 3 are of considerable antiquity. A study of them consists less of an examination of the current ground, but is in many cases confined to the record office. It is generally impossible to say what type of waterwheel might have been used, unless the mill site remains identifiable. All windmills are assumed to be post mills, due to the antiquity of most references. Those mills which remained into the 17th century could represent early examples of tower mills on Wirral, for these had certainly appeared in the country by the 16th century, if not considerably earlier. However, tower mills are generally considered to have been unknown on Wirral until the 18th century, and any assignment other than that of a post mill seems somewhat unlikely for these early sites.

Part 2 of this book discusses the mills covered from a partially industrial archaeological perspective, including for example, an examination of any known mechanical details. The mills marked on Burdett's survey and described in Part 2 are those which survived into the industrialised era. An industrial archaeological perspective cannot be given for many of the mills in Part 3, as working details are not known. Instead we must content ourselves with dates and approximate locations. Modern day descriptions of the sites have not been included in the majority of cases, unless I know that remains do exist. It has proved difficult to fully investigate the modern day topography at all of the locations listed. It might be that further earthworks, or even stonework, remain in some instances, still to be discovered by one with a keen archaeological eye. Part 3 is split into two chapters; all of the watermill sites have been considered first and then all of the windmill sites. In both chapters the mills have simply been ordered alphabetically.

CHAPTER 7: PRE-BURDETT WATERMILLS

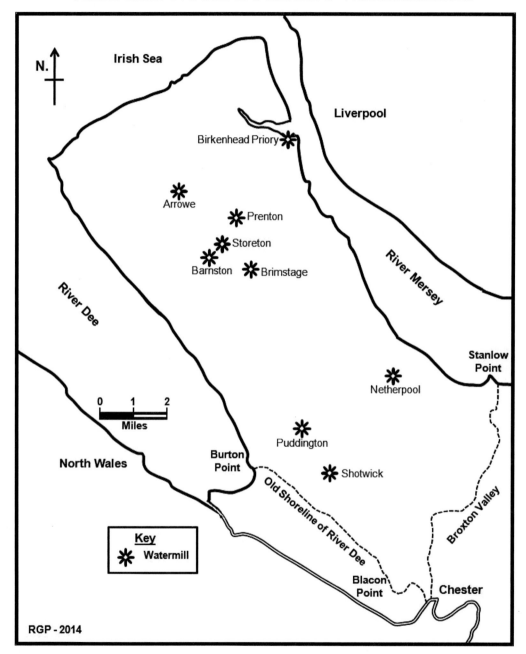

202. The watermills disused prior to Burdett's survey and covered in Part 3, Chapter 7.

7.1 Arrowe Mill

There is a 1347 reference in the Palatinate of Chester Forest Proceedings, to "*Arweymulne*", which Dodgson translated to mean the "mill at Arrowe". It is believed that this was a watermill and it must have been situated on the Arrowe Brook, for that is the only watercourse of any significance within the township. A potential mill pool is shown on the tithe map of 1846, evidently formed by damming Arrowe Brook. This pool was formerly within the grounds of Arrowe Hall, which was built by the Shaw family in 1835. It lies to the north of Nicholson's Plantation and remains a feature of Arrowe Park to this day.

It could be that this pool was not constructed when the grounds of Arrowe Hall were landscaped, for it may already have existed and could have originally been the mill pool. The pool is currently withheld by a large sandstone dam. One of the stone blocks near the bottom of this dam is inscribed with the date "1840", indicating the present dam to be contemporary to the construction of Arrowe Park by the Shaw family. However, this sandstone structure could represent a 19th century reconstruction of a much older dam. Therefore the pool could have a much older foundation than the rest of Arrowe Park and is possibly contemporary to the 14th century reference.

However, this pool is not shown on Burdett, Greenwood or Bryant's maps and I have not managed to locate any estate maps from before the Shaw family purchased the Arrowe estate in the 19th century. Even if the original dam was breached many centuries before the laying out of Arrowe Park, earthworks could have existed at that point, which led to the re-damming of the brook and the former pool being reinstated. However, this is purely supposition and no evidence of a watermill could be discerned downstream of the dam. It is unlikely that any remains of this mill exist in the heavily landscaped Arrowe Park, even below ground.

7.2 Barnston Mill

There was a medieval watermill in Barnston township. This is referred to in a document of 1376, mentioned in documentation associated with the Merseyside Historic Environment Record. This mill stood on Prenton Brook, which flows through the Barnston Dale Valley. Mitford Abraham said that it "stood close to the main road where it dips sharply into Barnston Dale". I only know of the one primary reference to this mill, and it is not covered by Dodgson. Bott also failed to provide any further reference. However, that it existed there is no doubt, for archaeological remains are more forthcoming.

A huge earthen bank runs across the valley of Barnston Dale, to the east of Barnston Road. This represents the mill dam and must have withheld a large body of water, although at some point in the past it has been breached, thus dispensing with the former mill pool. On Barnston Road, on the western side, is an old white cottage, which stands just north of Prenton Brook and is claimed locally to be the former mill house. This is shown on Bryant's map of 1831. The remaining evidence does not end there, for to the west of Barnston Road, on the other side to the mill dam, there are numerous dressed stones within the brook. Moving a distance downstream, the suspected remains of the mill can be seen. Ancient stonework may be seen on either side of the brook. In 2012 parts of this masonry stood to some six courses in height, but by 2014 building work was taking place on the stream bank and the remains had partially collapsed. Many worked stones may still be seen scattered in the brook itself.

These remains are long forgotten and to my knowledge are not recorded elsewhere. However, it seems highly likely that they must comprise the remains of Barnston mill, which would have been a small stone building. The remains seem to suggest that the mill itself was constructed above the brook, which implies working by an undershot wheel. These relics are a remarkable survivor, in an area where urbanisation is now not far away. Their continued existence seems to suggest that this mill must have survived for at least some centuries after the 14th century reference.

203. Surviving stonework on Prenton Brook at the suspected site of Barnston watermill. This wall has partially collapsed since this photograph was taken in 2012.

204. A cottage on Barnston Road which has been suggested to be the old mill house, or to stand on its site.

7.3 Birkenhead Priory Mill

There was formerly a watermill which was owned and operated by the monks of Birkenhead Priory. This was first mentioned in the 13th century and was situated on one of the streams which flowed into the southern side of Wallasey Pool. The 1291 taxation of Pope Nicholas IV mentions that Birkenhead Priory held land at Claughton and Moreton. A transcription of the taxation, in the *Cheshire Sheaf* of November 1962, relates that at Claughton "The Prior of Byrcheved…has there one mill which is worth per annum ……… 12s." Stewart-Brown writing in *Birkenhead Priory and the Mersey Ferry* analysed the taxation and found that – "in Claughton…the annual value of the area under cultivation (3 carucates) was thirty shillings, which was made up to £3 18s. 4d. by a small revenue from rents and the profits of a mill, the priory grange and timber". The banks of Wallasey Pool fell within Claughton cum Grange township and the priory watermill would have fallen within this area.

Another reference to the mill is in the Chester Recognizance Rolls and is dated 1330. At this date the prior named Robert had a disagreement with the lord of Seacombe, William Lasselles. According to Stewart-Brown "The complaint was that the prior and his man had, on the 6th May 1330, at the 'Mulne How' in Claughton, taken an anchor and a rope and kept them unjustly so that the complainants were losers to the amount £5. The prior's answer was that he was lord of the town of Claughton in right of his church and that he found...Seacombe men fastening the anchor and rope on his land at the 'Mulne How' where they had no right of common, so he seized the anchor and rope as it was lawful for him to do. To this the reply was that they were lords of the town of Seacombe and had a right of passage...across the Mersey, and that they were entitled to load and unload their boats and fasten the anchors at Wallasey Pool". The name *"Mulne How"* implies a mill related mound or hill and is the suggested position of the watermill, somewhere near to the shore of Wallasey Pool. In this instance Irvine suggested the mound would refer to the mill dam.

Further evidence that the mill lay on the shore of Wallasey Pool seems to be suggested by a petition document of 1305, from the prior of Birkenhead, who wished to enclose thirty acres of heath at Claughton, to Edward Prince of Wales. This is quoted in the *Cheshire Sheaf* in December 1948 and gives the boundaries of the prior's enclosure as "from the road from Budstane to the mill of Birkenhead and from that road to the Pool of Walleye". Irvine pointed out that this shows the mill must have been on the shore of Wallasey Pool, thus dispensing with older beliefs that this mill had been sited on Tranmere Pool.

A national valuation survey of ecclesiastical wealth, *Valor Ecclesiasticus*, was ordered by Henry VIII and conducted in the first half of 1535, shortly before the dissolution. The assessment of Birkenhead Priory's possessions was published by Stewart-Brown and makes reference to "Birket Grange and demesnes, the watermill and ferry boat", which were valued at £9. Mortimer, in his *The History of the Hundred of Wirral*, printed the untranslated form of "the watermill and ferry boat" as *"Molendio aquatico et le Feribot"*. Following the dissolution of Birkenhead Priory in 1536, its land and property including the watermill were confiscated and became the property of the Crown. The priory's former estate was then looked after by a royal bailiff.

Henry VIII established the Court of Augmentations, later the Augmentation Office, to administer confiscated monastic property. Mortimer printed a return from the Court of Augmentations for 1544, which gives the annual value of the priory watermill as 20s. In 1545, the priory lands passed from Crown ownership, when Ralph Worsley, described as "the king's servant", obtained by grant from Henry VIII, lands in Birkenhead and Claughton. Details of this grant were published in the *Cheshire Sheaf* in January 1923. Worsley was granted considerable local property for £568 11s. 6d. including "all the house and site and all the church spire and cemetery of the lately dissolved Priory of Birkenhead, as well as all the houses, buildings, mills, granges...including the house and lands in the occupation of Robert Mollyneux and a pigeon house, a mill, the fish yards...the ferry and the ferry house and the ferry bote". Worsley was part of Henry VIII's own household and had once been the Keeper of Lions at the Tower of London.

Ralph Worsley died in 1573, after which his estate passed to Alice, his daughter. She was his only heiress following the deaths of her two sisters. Alice Worsley later married Thomas Powell of Horsley, into whose property the priory watermill was then incorporated. A watermill was mentioned in an inquisition post mortem into the death of Thomas Powell in 1635. The mill certainly existed into at least the 17th century, and is mentioned in a 1646 document related to the Birkenhead ferry service. The mill appears several times in the 'Sequestrators' Accounts for Wirral' in the period 1644-1648, which were published in the *Cheshire Sheaf* in 1956. In 1644 Sir Thomas Powell received £1 from Henry Moores for the watermill; this Thomas Powell was Alice Worsley's grandson. Several months later in the same year, he paid £1 9s. 6d. "to Richard Charnock, Thomas Christopher and Gilbert Wilson for 28 days worke on makeinge of a bridge at the Water Mill and for nailes to the said work".

Further extracts from the Sequestrators' Accounts were printed in the *Cheshire Sheaf* in December 1948 by Irvine. These show that Henry Moores paid a further £3 rent to Sir Thomas Powell in 1646. The last known reference to the mill is in the accounts for 1647 under the title "Sir Thomas Powell's racke rents at mid-summer 1647 for the demesne lands". In these rents Henry Moores paid a further 15s. "for ye Water Mill". No reference to the Birkenhead Priory watermill has been found after this and it had probably already disappeared by the turn of the 18th century. A man of the name Henry Moore died in 1647 and was buried at Bebington. It could be that this was the miller; in which case the watermill may have ceased to work after his death.

The stream on which this mill was located was probably the Bridge End Brook, which entered Wallasey Pool at a point off Bridge Street, near to Egerton Dock. Irvine believed this to be the only stream sizeable enough to have powered the mill. The other main stream to enter Wallasey Pool, on its Claughton bank, was the Gill Brook. This entered the pool east of the Bridge End Brook, but was not so large. The Bridge End Brook is shown on Lawton's plan of 1824; it enters Wallasey Pool at a point marked "Bridge End". The stream is also shown on Bryant's map of 1831, and in further detail on Bennison's *Map of Liverpool and Environs* dated 1835.

Bennison shows that the brook flowed into the pool at a small inlet, which extended up to Bridge Street. Corporation Road was carried over this inlet by a bridge. It has been suggested that the mill lay near this point. Irvine writing in the *Cheshire Sheaf* in December 1948, postulated that Bridge Street in Birkenhead, was formerly carried over the mouth of the Bridge End Brook by an embankment. This embankment probably lay upon the medieval mill dam; a suggestion which is to some extent supported by Bennison's map.

Despite Irvine suggesting a position on Wallasey Pool, Allison writing in *Sidelights on Tranmere* said that – "Several reasons suggest that the site of the Priory water mill may well have been near Victoria Road: here the stream began to flow faster over a sandstone outcrop after receiving additional water from a small brook on its left bank…The Priory owned a water mill, though its site is unknown". Allison's reasoning seems to have been partially based upon a group of five fields called "Dam Hay". These are shown on the Tranmere township tithe map of 1843, and lay in the vicinity of Victoria Road. This location was once near to Tranmere Pool, although somewhat further inland. It is not related to the suspected site of the priory watermill, as described on Wallasey Pool, although it may indicate the site of a second mill.

It is certain that the mill site near to Wallasey Pool would have been partially tidal in nature. The tide mills on Wallasey Pool, as mentioned in Part 2, were substantially further inland, and prove that portion of the pool to have been affected by the tides into the 19th century. Therefore, it is not unjustified to conclude that the priory watermill could well have been successfully operated as a tide mill. The mill dam denoted by Bridge Street withheld a pool, which could have been filled by the incoming tide as well as by the Bridge End Brook. It seems likely that at a position so close to the mouth of the Mersey, the mill pool must have had significant tidal influence, but it is not known to what extent the tides were harnessed and employed.

7.4 Brimstage Mill

In 1278 the Palatinate of Chester Forest Proceedings make reference to "*unum molendinum*", that is "one mill", in Brimstage township. This reference is reproduced from Dodgson. It is believed that this was a medieval watermill, although it is of a similar age to the earliest known instances of windmills in Cheshire. It has been suggested that there was once both a watermill and a windmill in Brimstage. A site for the Brimstage windmill is postulated in the section on Thornton Hough mill.

The Brimstage township tithe map of c.1842 includes the field names "Mill Hey" and "Mill Way", in a four field group of mill fields, north of Brimstage Road and at a point diagonally opposite Brimstage Hall. A small stream lies to the south of these fields, the same stream which follows Brimstage Road through Brimstage village. It seems debatable whether a stream of this small size could ever have reliably powered a watermill, although Bott felt that "a watermill site seems probable". If a watermill did indeed exist in this township, this is probably the location contemporary to the 1278 reference, for there are no other streams, or convincing field names.

7.5 Netherpool Mills

Overpool and Netherpool township holds the site of at least one ancient watermill and possibly several, although no definite site has ever been satisfactorily determined. Dodgson provided some ancient references to mills in this township; the earliest is an inquisition post mortem dated 1308 which lists one watermill as "*unum molendinum aquaticum*". An English abstract of this inquisition was published in the Public Record Office's *Calendar of Inquisitions Post Mortem*. The enquiry was into the death of James de Pulle, who had "A messuage, 2 carucates land, and a water-mill, held of Joan daughter of Hugh de Tydringtone" in "Nethere Pulle". Another document of around a century later is one of the charters in the John Rylands collection, this provides a 1402 reference to "*le molyn de Pullé*", that is "the mill of Poole". The same document of 1402 mentions "*le Grauntpoll*" in connection with the mill, which Dodgson translated as "the great pool or stream". The Chartulary of St. Werburgh's Abbey records an agreement in Netherpool between the abbot and Robert de Poole. A translation of the Latin was published by the Chetham Society in 1923. The agreement dated 1272 involved Robert making "a bridge or causeway over...The Wolfpool"; he was forbidden from "putting up any mill or other buildings, to have the benefit of the water" as it was felt this might interfere with the monks who needed to allow their livestock to drink.

A writer in the *Cheshire Sheaf* in November 1950 stated that – "The Poole Mills seem to have been situated on the little stream which divides Nether Poole township from Hooton. In Bryant's Map…two mill pools appear to be shewn a few hundred yards west of the site which until a few years ago was occupied by Poole Hall". These pools no longer exist and they may have been fish ponds, situated as they were by such an ancient residence. There is nothing to establish that they were definitely mill pools. However, Bryant's map of 1831 rather interestingly marks a building as "Mill House", on the lane which then ran between the villages of Poole and Whitby. Directly opposite, Bryant also marks a "Mill Lane", which runs west towards Great Sutton. The mill house cannot be identified on the Overpool and Netherpool township tithe map, but in a similar area is a group of four mill fields named "Rushy Mill field", "Pyes Mill field" and "Mill Hey". The brook which runs through the Rivacre Valley lies to the north and it seems likely that these fields show the approximate locality of a watermill in the township. Modern development now overlies the area.

There is a further group of three mill fields to the south, on the other side of Overpool and Netherpool township, near to the boundary with Great Sutton. These might have a different origin, and Rivacre Brook lies to the west. The fields are called "Mill Post" and "Mill Brow", and the road which crosses Rivacre Brook nearby is still called Mill Lane. This is the western end of the lane marked on Bryant's map. It could be that this represents another watermill site, although Bott felt that "a windmill site seems more likely". Alternatively, these field names could originate from the road name Mill Lane. The origins of the road name surely lie near its eastern end, where Bryant marked "Mill House", so this may not be a true mill site. Further fields, also now built upon, were "Big Mill Hay" and "Little Mill Hay", which lay in Whitby township, to the south west of Overpool Station. Dodgson provided a 1708 reference to "Milne Hey" in Whitby township, which may be related. These fields are near to the second group described in Overpool and Netherpool township, and presumably commemorate the same feature. However, the Whitby fields are a significant distance east of Rivacre Brook, which may support Bott's suggestion that this is actually a windmill site.

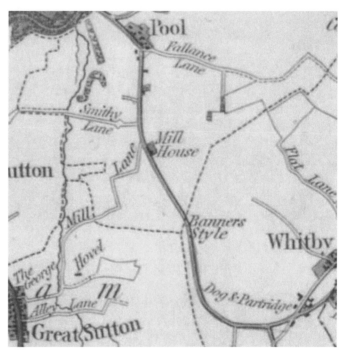

205. Bryant clearly marked a "Mill Lane" leading into Great Sutton and also a "Mill House", yet the mill from which these names are derived must have disappeared long before 1831. The tithe map shows two groups of mill fields, one north of Mill House, and another towards the western end of Mill Lane.

7.6 Prenton Mill

The Domesday survey of 1086 records two watermills on Wirral. The first, as mentioned in Part 2, was listed as a component of the "Manor of Estham", and may well have occupied the same site as Bromborough mill. The second mill was listed within the "Manor of Prestune", which was held by Walter de Vernon in Domesday times. The survey, as translated by Tait in *The Domesday Survey of Cheshire*, notes that "There is a mill serving the hall" ("*ibi molinum seruiens curiae*"). It could well be that a mill stood here in Anglo-Saxon times. Before the Norman takeover the manor of Prenton had been held by Wulfgeat, Eadric and Luvede, who had subdivided it into three smaller manors.

There are not many rivers present in this township and Prenton mill must have stood on the brook running through the small valley of Prenton Dell, to the south of the village. Mitford Abraham said that Prenton mill had "been disused for many centuries" in 1903, whilst Marriott writing for *Cheshire Life* in 1952 claimed that "the mill ceased working some five centuries ago". Milling was certainly still being carried out in 1608, for in the will of John Bruerton, printed by Beazley in the *Cheshire Sheaf* in February 1925, a debt of £4 was owed to "the milner of Prenton milne". This is the last known record of this mill, which is not shown on Burdett's map of 1777, or any other survey of Cheshire. It seems likely that other references to this mill must exist given the only ones known are in the 11th and 17th centuries, a considerable interlude.

Amazingly, a remnant of the last incarnation of this mill still existed in the early years of the last century. Writing his 'Notes on the Old Halls of Wirral' in 1900 Irvine commented, when writing about Prenton Hall – "In the account given in Domesday Book, mention is made of a mill which supplies the Hall, no doubt the predecessor of this very building... At first sight it seemed highly improbable that a water-mill could ever have existed in this township, and yet, on a careful search being made, hidden away in a dingle, a few hundred yards from the Hall, were found the remains of a mill dam which, when complete, must have blocked the end of a little valley – through which still runs a small stream – and formed a fine sheet of water". Prenton Hall lies a little way to the east of the river on which the mill stood.

Further reference was made to this discovery by Rideout in his paper on 'Wirral Watersheds and River Systems and their influence on Local History' dated 1922. He said – "Irvine was the first to notice the peculiar bank at the end of the dale, now broken in two places, and to suggest that this possibly was the site of the mill...I have more recently examined the spot carefully and think there is little doubt that this bank is of artificial construction, and it seems reasonable to conclude that it represents the remnant of the ancient mill dam... this is the only possible site for a mill dam within the township of Prenton, so that it does not seem to be stretching the facts too much to conclude that the Dell was formerly the site for the mill dam".

There are no mill related field names listed on the Prenton township tithe map of c.1845. However, the map does record an interesting feature, which appears to be the trace of an in-filled mill pool, on the brook already mentioned. This feature falls within the wooded region of Prenton Dell yet it has no tree cover itself. Ordnance Survey maps record how the area eventually became wooded, such that by 1910 it was virtually indistinguishable from the rest of the Dell. Today the bank of the mill dam has a trackway built upon it and the area is somewhat disturbed, although a marshy hollow which may be the partial site of the mill pool can still be discerned.

206. Plot 82 on the Prenton township tithe map adjoins the brook in Prenton Dell and is a peculiar shape. It may preserve the outline of an in-filled mill pool. (Courtesy of Cheshire Archives and Local Studies)

7.7 Puddington Mill

There is an ancient watermill site on Shotwick Brook, in Puddington township. This is mentioned in an inquisition of 1369, which refers to alterations being made to a local road. Brownbill's translation of the document was published in the *Cheshire Sheaf* in June 1942, and states that – "It is not to the loss or injury of the Earl of Chester or any one else if Hamon de Mascy of Podynton be allowed to vary a certain road leading between the Earl's park of Shotewyk…as far as the said Hamon's mill pool…and he may be allowed to have and repair said water mill pool and the mill itself in a place called Depedale in Podynton within the forest of Wyrhale and to hold the same so repaired for himself and his heirs for ever". This inquisition is the major known reference to this watermill, which seems to have been in the ownership of the Massey family of Puddington Old Hall. A second potential reference to this mill, which is earlier in date, is in the The Record Society of Lancashire and Cheshire's *Cheshire Forest Eyre Roll 1357*. In the plea roll of 1357 Puddington mill is referred to as a landmark, the position of a field in Puddington being referred to as "towards the mill". This shows that there must have been a mill in Puddington at the time of the eyre in 1357, and it was probably the same watermill as that mentioned in the 1369 inquisition. Land within the field mentioned in the eyre was held by "Hamo de Mascy", who also owned Puddington watermill.

Shotwick Brook runs parallel to Parkgate Road in Puddington township, before eventually turning to the east and running towards the township of Shotwick. The Puddington township tithe map of 1839 marks a group of seven fields, all relating to a dam, on either side of Shotwick Brook, between Puddington Lane and the Parkgate Road/Welsh Road junction. Rideout mentioned these fields in his paper on 'Wirral Field Names' in 1923; pointing out that there are various dam related field names here – "Dam Hey", "Little Dam Hey" etc., he stated that – "the Dam Heys…lie on Shotwick Brook, where earthworks that may once have been a dam can still be traced".

The relics of this dam are not actually within the Dam Hey fields themselves, but a little further south. A writer in the *Cheshire Sheaf* in July 1942 recalled seeing them around 1912 – "Just before the brook reaches the Puddingon – Shotwick boundary it turns S.E., and at this point there can still be seen (or could when I was there 30 years ago) the substantial remains of the Mill Dam." I believe that these traces may still remain today, although when I examined the area I was unable to locate any obvious remains.

7.8 Shotwick Mill

Another medieval watermill existed in Shotwick township, only a little further down Shotwick Brook from Puddington mill and at a position just north of Shotwick Lane. Very little is known about the history of this mill, which is mentioned by Beazley in his 'Notes on Shotwick', as published in the *Transactions of the Historic Society of Lancashire and Cheshire* in 1913 – "a disused and grassy road leads to Shotwick brook and the dam of an old water-mill now pulled down. The dam is a large one, and the mill pond must have covered a considerable area; of its history however, if it has any, nothing has been discovered".

The only contemporary reference known to refer to this mill is in Beazley's translation of one of the Chester plea rolls, dated to the 30th year of the reign of Edward I, that is 1302. This document is related to Cecily, wife of Robert de Hockenhull, who "sued Thomas, son of Robert de Hockenhall, for…one third of two parts of one water-mill in Shotewyk". It seems likely that this reference relates to the watermill site mentioned on Shotwick Brook and suggests that it is of great age. The Shotwick township tithe map of c.1848 also marks a field called "Little Mill Field" adjacent to the site where Beazley describes the mill dam.

The mill at Shotwick was provided with a substantial mill pool and Marriott, writing for *Cheshire Life* in 1952, claimed that "Shotwick Mill had one of the finest dams in the peninsula, and at the turn of the last century the old pool still proved a lure to many a fisherman, but no masonry existed even then". This statement actually seems rather unfounded, for the dam at Shotwick was evidently breached many years ago, and none of the early surveys of Cheshire marks a pool here. The trackway described by Beazley still exists and leads to an earthen bank of great proportions; obviously of artificial construction, this crosses the river valley to this day. This mill dam has been destroyed at one point, thus allowing the Shotwick Brook to flow through. Behind the dam, low lying land, which has remained marshy, denotes the site of the old mill pool. The little used trackway which leads to the mill site from Shotwick Lane must be an ancient path and is very wide, showing it to have been a more important route in past centuries. The route appears to be partially artificial in nature, forming a sort of embankment above Shotwick Brook, via which carts could perhaps once have descended to the mill.

207. A well constructed culvert on Shotwick Brook at the site of Shotwick watermill.

Rather surprisingly the site still holds significant remains, despite the paucity of historical details available on this mill. Contrary to Marriott's statement, stonework exists to this day. The remains of the culvert, which carried water to the waterwheel after it had passed through the mill dam, still exist. This culvert has a fine little archway of dressed sandstone, with a substantial keystone and stonework standing to some seven courses. It runs some yards to the site of the mill itself, just below the dam. The length of the culvert allows the wide trackway from Shotwick Lane to sweep around and cross Shotwick Brook.

At its far extreme the culvert is ruinous and partially collapsed. The brook here is lined with stone walls, whilst much additional worked sandstone lies displaced within the watercourse. This stonework must surely be related to the site of the mill itself. It would seem that this mill probably employed an undershot waterwheel and it must have been a very small building. Given the small size of the stream and ancient nature of the site, the waterwheel may have been directly in the flow of the brook, for there is no evidence of any subsidiary leat. An old quarry stands adjacent to the mill; a significant quantity of sandstone has been removed from here, possibly including the stone used in the mill's construction. This is an important site which has survived in a forgotten, little disrupted state, for many centuries. It is difficult to put a date on the surviving remains, but they must be centuries in age.

208. The other end of the culvert, which is unfortunately disintegrating, as seen in 2014.

Norris suggested an interesting possibility, that this could have operated as a tide mill, in his account of 'The Water-Powered Corn Mills of Cheshire'. He stated that "It is possible that this was a tide mill before the silting up of the Dee estuary". The Dee silted up at Shotwick many centuries ago, but I am not convinced how influenced by the tide such a small stream would ever have been at this distance inland, which is not inconsiderable. The surviving mill dam suggests that a large reserve of water accumulated in a more conventional manner, irrespective of any minor tidal influence.

Mitford Abraham provided a different location for Shotwick mill which he said "lay just north of the Castle" and a river does indeed flow at this location. This opinion is repeated by Stewart-Brown in his 'The Royal Manor and Park of Shotwick'; he said "There are frequent mentions in old deeds of a mill at Shotwick, and we are told by Mr. Elton that a water-mill lay just north of the Castle". It would seem that other primary references to this mill are in existence, but these were not published in the sources I have examined, for I have only found the single reference given by Beazley. The location previously described is certainly the primary mill site in Shotwick township, even if just based on the surviving remains. However, it could be that there was another mill associated with the Norman Castle, although if so no documentary references or physical remains are known. Bott said in reference to the castle mill that he had found no "corroborative documentary or archaeological evidence".

7.9 Storeton Mill

Reference has already been made to an inquisition post mortem of 1284, which records a windmill in Storeton, one of the earliest references to a windmill in the area. The same inquisition also mentions the watermill of Storeton as *"molendinum de Storton"* according to Dodgson, for there was both a windmill and a watermill in the township at this date. An abstract of this inquisition was published in English by the Public Record Office in their *Calendar of Inquisitions Post Mortem*. The inquisition mentions that in Storeton there were "2 carucates land in demesne, a windmill, a watermill, and 9l. 3s. 11d. rent of assize". Dodgson also referenced a charter in the John Rylands collection which mentions *"molendinum versus Stortona"*; this is dated 1260-1280 and may refer to the watermill here.

The watermill of Storeton is then mentioned in a charter of 1295 which was printed in the *Cheshire Sheaf* in December 1956. The charter deals with a share in Storeton watermill belonging to the widow, Agnes de Schouresworth. It was stated in the *Cheshire Sheaf* in December 1956 that she was likely one of the heiresses of Sir Philip de Bamville Knight, who had died in 1283, and in whose inquisition post mortem the watermill and windmill were mentioned. The charter suggests that Agnes married into the Schouresworth family and was widowed, prior to her subsequent marriage to John de Becheton.

The charter reads that – "This is the agreement made between Agnes relict of William de Schouresworth and William de Stanleg'…namely that Agnes is pure widowhood and… lets…to the said William all her part which she has etc. in a certain pool (stagnum) and site (situm) of a watermill of Storeton' in Wyrale for the term of twenty years ensuring the term to begin at the feast of St. Michael in the 23rd year of the reign of King Edward". This 1295 reference is the last certain mention of Storeton watermill. There is an indenture dated 1348, dealing with the manor of Storeton, and published in the *Cheshire Sheaf* in January 1944. The third share of the manor inherited by Agnes de Becheton, was being passed to her son Simon de Becheton, and there is a reference to mills in the plural. This seems to be because a share was granted in all manorial mills, irrespective of how many mills there were, since Storeton windmill might have been the only one present. The *Cheshire Sheaf*, in September 1956, gave abstracts of the inquisitions post mortem into the deaths of the cousins William de Lakene and Simon de Becheton, both of whom died around 1349. The inquisitions mention that each held a third of the manor of Storeton, including a third of Storeton windmill. However, there is no reference to either having a share in Storeton watermill, indicating that it was probably no longer operational by the mid-14th century.

The site of Storeton watermill is suspected to be in the vicinity of Landican Lane, at the point where it is intercepted by Prenton Brook. Landican Lane is an ancient route, indeed if this is the site of the watermill we may assume the lane dates to at least the 13th century. The lane at this point is unusually wide given its current function, suggesting it was formerly of some greater significance. The stream flows underneath Landican Lane by means of a twin culvert of square section. This seems to be an ancient structure, built of local sandstone and very substantial in nature. It has been suggested by local archaeologist Peter France that marshy land to the south of Landican Lane represents the site of the mill pool, where a visible depression might be observed. The mill itself is thought to have stood within the field to the north of the lane.

209. A large culvert which passes under Landican Lane and takes the waters of Prenton Brook to the site of Storeton mill.

210. Fields by Landican Lane at the suspected site of Storeton watermill, as examined in 2012.

CHAPTER 8: PRE-BURDETT WINDMILLS

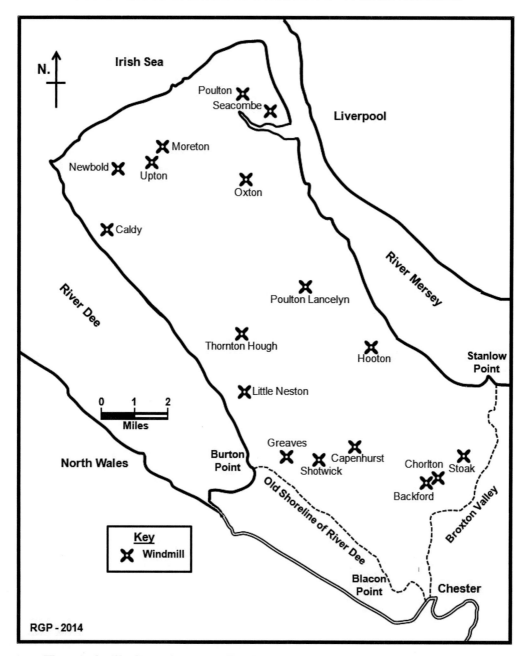

211. The windmills disused prior to Burdett's survey and covered in Part 3, Chapter 8.

8.1 Caldy Mill

Caldy mill was a post mill, which once stood in Caldy township, some distance south of Grange mill. This township has a long association with windmills and probably contains several sites. The rental of Thomas Norris of Speke, who owned land in Caldy, is dated 1454 and was printed in the *Cheshire Sheaf* in April 1908. One of the names recorded in the Norris rental is "The Mylne Way", suggesting a mill in the vicinity at that time, although one is not specifically mentioned. Brownbill noted in *West Kirby and Hilbre* that, "The Mylne Way…may…refer to a mill which seems to have stood southwest of the village, about half-way down the river-side". This name survived in 1639, for according to Dodgson "the Millway" was mentioned at that date.

The earliest known reference to the windmill itself at Caldy is an inquisition taken at Chester in 1553. A transcription of this inquisition was printed by Beazley in *Thurstaston in Cheshire*. This relates that "John Whytmore was seised of the manor of Thurstaston and lands etc. there, and of 24 messuages, windmill, 400 ac. land etc. in Caulday in the hundred of Wyrrihall". An ancestor of John, William Whitmore, had held land in Caldy in the Norris rental of a century earlier. John Whitmore bought the Norris's share of Caldy in 1514. In 1644 "Caldy Hey and Mill" were owned by another member of the family, Valentine Whitmore of Thurstaston. Valentine Whitmore was a Royalist who surrendered himself during the Civil War and later petitioned in London in April 1646, as recorded in the *Cheshire Sheaf* in July 1896. He was fined a sixth of his estate, which in total was valued at £277 10s. and included, "one windmill lying in Chaldee", valued at £10. To calculate the fine imposed Valentine Whitmore's estate was valued in detail. The valuation includes a list of his tenants in Little Caldy in 1644, which was printed by Beazley. One item which was valued was "The Mill", £5 rent for which was "payable at Martinmas and Candlemas". In May 1646 Valentine Whitmore married Elizabeth Glegg of Gayton, and in 1648 he surrendered the manors of Thurstaston and Caldy, including Caldy windmill, to Edward Glegg, his brother-in-law.

This mill is marked on Captain Greenville Collins's survey of the River Dee, conducted during the 1680s and published in 1689. It shows both Grange and Caldy mills; the latter is clearly labelled "Cauldy Mill". Collins's chart is accompanied with a description, this section from 1686 reads – "Being on the back of the Hyle Sand, bring the mill (at Little Caldy) and the wood (at Grange Hall) one on the other and run in, keeping close along the Hyle Sand and so into High Lake, and anchor". This mill is that which was owned by the Whitmores and it may have been a different structure, on a different site, to the mill suggested by the Norris rental.

The mill is also shown on Mackay-Math's survey of 1732; it is some way south of the two mills which this chart marks at Grange. The mill continued to be marked on sea charts into the latter half of the 18th century. For example, it is shown on Fearon and Eyes's chart, they surveyed this sea coast in 1736-1737, and is also shown on Williamson's chart of 1766. In 1771 Peter Burdett produced *A Chart of the Harbour of Liverpool*; on this chart Grange mill is shown, but Caldy mill is not. Of course, nautical charts aimed to show landmarks useful for navigation, rather than all landmarks present, so this does not necessarily mean the mill had disappeared by this date. Some years later, in 1772-1774 Burdett did the survey work for his *A Survey of the County Palatine of Chester*. This map does not show any mill at Caldy, nor does Greenwood's map of 1819. There is a chance that this mill was erroneously omitted from these surveys, for this was the case with Grange mill. However, it seems unlikely that Caldy mill survived into the 19th century and it may well have gone by the 1770s.

212. *The symbol of a mill is drawn to the right of the word "Caldy" on this chart surveyed by Fearon and Eyes.*

Writing in *West Kirby and Hilbre* Brownbill commented that – "Caldy Mill was once, like Grange Mill, a mark for mariners making for the Hoyle Lake as a haven. It...appears to have stood on the easterly side of Caldy, perhaps above the manor-house. It has disappeared entirely." Brownbill seems to have believed that the windmill which lasted into the 18th century and that inferred by the Norris rental represented distinct sites. Yet another mill site was identified by Irvine who suggested to Brownbill, in reference to the Norris rental, that – "an earlier mill may have stood a short distance to the north, beside the West Kirby and Caldy Road". As an alternative to Brownbill's location on the east side of Caldy, field name evidence tends to point at mill sites nearer the coast, to the south of the village itself.

Caldy township contains sixteen mill field names in three distinct and separate groups. These may indicate the positions of multiple windmill sites and Bott felt that three sites were likely in Caldy. The most northerly group is the "Mill Looms" ("Lower Croft Mill Looms", "Top Mill Looms" etc.), which form an eight field group. Dodgson felt that "Croft Mill Looms" represented a corruption of a "Croft Melayne" mentioned in the Norris rental, where Mellon referred to "narrow strips of land", so this may not be a mill site at all. This identification is supported by a field on the tithe map adjoining the "Mill Looms", but retaining its uncorrupted name, for it is called "Higher Croft Mellon". To the south of the "Mill Looms" is a six field group of "Mill Hays" which certainly seems to be suggestive of a mill site topographically and further south still a two field group, also "Mill Hays". The large group of six "Mill Hays" must certainly represent a windmill site, possibly that which existed into the 18th century. A road called Mill Hey Road has been built upon some of these fields. All of the land where the tithe map shows mill fields has now been built upon and the sites of Caldy's windmills must now be covered by housing.

8.2 Capenhurst Mill

Records of a windmill in Capenhurst are scarce, but the plea roll of the 1357 eyre records that a windmill, "*unum molendinum ventriticum*", was built there c.1336. The plea is printed in *Cheshire Forest Eyre Roll 1357* as "21 years ago, the ancestors of Thomas [de Capenhurst] constructed a windmill at the same place which is to the harm of the beasts. Therefore it is to be forfeited and destroyed, price of the mill 40s. 0d., and concerning the value of the same it is half a mark for each year from the time it was built, for which Thomas, who occupies it, will answer". John de Capenhurst had constructed the mill, but had subsequently died, leaving Thomas liable for it.

The next known reference is over one and a half centuries later, for an indenture dated 1517 records that a mill existed in Capenhurst at that time. This indenture is listed in Volume 6 of *A Descriptive Catalogue of Ancient Deeds* and records the grant of land to Elizabeth, the wife of the late Richard Cholmondeley. Elizabeth was granted for life "the manor of Capenhurst and all the messuages, lands, &c, there and in Chorley, Malpas, Egge, Larton and Bikerton (except a windmill in Capenhurst)". A third reference is provided by Ormerod in his *History* of Cheshire. He gave a transcription for an inquisition post mortem of 1597, into the death of Sir Hugh Cholmondeley Knight, who "held two-thirds of the manor of Capenhurst, with seven messuages, eight cottages, one windmill". No reference is known to this mill after the 16th century and it is not known if the 14th century and 16th century mills occupied the same site. Bryant showed a "Mill Lane" running to Capenhurst from Ledsham, on his map of 1831. This is now Rectory Lane and seems to denote the probable vicinity in which a mill stood.

Bott drew attention to the fact that a windmill is shown to the south east of Willaston, on both John Speed's map of Cheshire dated 1610 and also on Robert Morden's map of Cheshire dated 1695. These surveys were drawn at a small scale, and are inaccurate in terms of showing such features as mills, hence why they have gone unmentioned and Burdett's survey is the first which this book has depended upon. For instance Speed's map shows just two windmills on Wirral, definitely an underestimate and both are hard to pinpoint to a specific site! Bott too considered these surveys "doubtful"; but it is just possible that the mill shown below Willaston could be that at Capenhurst.

213. Bryant shows "Mill Lane" as the road linking Ledsham and Capenhurst; this is now Rectory Lane.

In Capenhurst township, there are seven mill related field names shown on the tithe map of c.1840. Firstly, there are two adjoining fields south of Chapel Lane named "Mill Field" and "Mill Field Croft". Those fields of most interest consist of a five field group of "Mill Hays" ("Pikes or Big Mill Hay", "Little Mill Hay" etc.). These lie scattered on either side of Rectory Lane (Bryant's Mill Lane) and it seems likely that they must indicate the site of the 16th century Capenhurst windmill, and possibly also the site of the 14th century mill, unless this is shown by the other two fields. There are few other satisfactory explanations for this large group of mill fields. Remarkably there is a "Mill Hey Farm" on Rectory Lane to this day, just on the edge of this group of fields.

214. Mill Hey Farm, which stands on Rectory Lane in the vicinity of the likely site of Capenhurst windmill.

8.3 Chorlton and Backford Mills

There was once a windmill in Chorlton township and another in the adjoining township of Backford. Both of these sites were in the parish of Backford, less than two miles apart, and due to their close proximity they have been examined together. The Palatinate of Chester Forest Proceedings refer to *"molendinum ventricitum"*, that is "the windmill", in Chorlton township in 1392. This reference is reproduced from Dodgson. A further reference may be found in a rent roll from 1398, a transcription of which was printed in the *Cheshire Sheaf* in August 1912. This roll lists rents paid to Henry Sutton, the abbot of St. Werburgh's Abbey at that time. It makes reference to a windmill in Chorlton, under the rents payable for that township. Another reference in this vicinity is in *Lancashire & Cheshire Church Surveys 1649-1655*. This contains transcriptions detailing various adjacent pieces of land, which were owned by the Dean and Chapter of Chester in 1649. The first of these was "One Close of Arrable land, commonly called the Mill Crofft.."; and the second "One Close of Arrable land called the Mill Feild butting Eastwards to the highway to Backford and west to Mollington Lane". Most interesting is the third piece of land – "One little parcell of ground whereon the Windmill stood, near the South End of the said feild which now lieth waste". Assuming these fields were in the same vicinity as each other, the location of the second piece of land seems to suggest a site between Backford and Mollington. The third plot of land shows that the windmill mentioned was no longer in existence in 1649, but suggests it might have stood within living memory for those alive in the mid-17th century.

Further indirect reference to mills may be found in field names, within both Chorlton and Backford townships. Dodgson mentioned that a document dated 1637 in the Cholmondeley family deeds refers to "The Mill Hay" in Chorlton township. The Chorlton township tithe map of c.1849 shows a five field group of fields named "Mill Hill", to the east of Poplar

Hall Lane and in the vicinity of Mount Farm. Poplar Hall Lane forms the boundary of Chorlton and Backford townships and the Backford township tithe map of c.1842 lists a further two mill fields, "Long Mill Croft" and "Mill Field", opposite those in Chorlton. Such a large group of mill related field names certainly suggests a likely windmill site, and this may well be the site of the 14th century windmill in Chorlton township. None of these fields have been built upon, so it could be that archaeological evidence remains to prove whether this is a true mill site.

The windmill site mentioned in the church survey appears to be a second site in Backford, unrelated to the 14th century windmill in Chorlton. There are two mill related field names on the tithe map, in the south of Backford, next to Backford Brook and north of the Shropshire Union Canal. Bott felt that "a watermill site is probable", based on the fact that these fields were by the brook. However, these fields are called "Mill Croft" and "Mill Field" and this appears to be a wonderful example of the preservation of field names through the centuries. The two fields lie next to each other and there seems little doubt that they must represent the "Mill Crofft" and "Mill Feild" of the 1649 church survey. The proof comes from the location of the "Mill Feild" given in that survey. The "Mill Field" on the tithe map borders Station Road to the west, which before the coming of the railway, must have been Mollington Lane. On the eastern side lies Rake Lane and this is undoubtedly "the highway to Backford". The 17th century description applies to this site so well, that the site of that windmill must surely lie somewhere in this vicinity. The church survey seems to imply that the site was in the southern part of "Mill Feild". That field has now been intersected by the Shropshire Union Canal to the south, so the actual site could be lost.

A primary reference to a windmill in Backford was discovered late in my researches. *Cheshire Inquisitions Post Mortem: Stuart Period 1603-1660* mentions a mill here, which probably stood at the site just described, as mentioned in the church survey. The inquisition dated 1614 is into the death of Henry Birkenhead of Backford, who died in 1613. Henry Birkenhead had acquired the manor of Backford in 1571, and could have had this mill built, unless it already existed when he obtained the manor. A windmill evidently existed in Backford as early as 1597, for the inquisition post mortem gives details of a fine levied in that year on Henry Birkenhead and his wife Elizabeth. There is reference to "a windmill in Backford, to the use of Henry Birkenhead, senr. until Christmas next following the date of the indenture & then to the use of Alice Singleton, now the wife of Henry Birkenhead, junr., for life." So a windmill stood in Backford in the late 16th century, which was held by the Birkenhead family, the lords of the manor at that time. It was initially held by Henry Birkenhead who died in 1613, and then by his son's wife Alice Singleton.

Hence, there seem to be two distinct windmill sites in close proximity to each other, one in the township of Chorlton and one in Backford. It was initially tempting to assume that the 17th century church survey referred to the mill at Chorlton which was mentioned in the 14th century. The connection seemed particularly valid given Chorlton windmill is listed on a rent roll of St. Werburgh's and the site of Backford windmill was owned by the Dean and Chapter of Chester in 1649. It seemed likely that the monastic windmill, or its site, could have descended to the Dean and Chapter of Chester Cathedral after the dissolution of St. Werburgh's Abbey. However, the site identified via the church survey is in the most south easterly corner of Backford township and is not especially near the boundary with Chorlton township, so it is hard to see how this could be the site of Chorlton mill. The discovery of the 1614 inquisition post mortem confirmed that there was a windmill in Backford as well as Chorlton. These mills may have been short-lived and since the references to them are around two centuries apart, it is unlikely they existed simultaneously. Chorlton mill was monastically owned in the late 14th century, whilst Backford mill was owned by the Birkenhead family around the turn of the 17th century, but had already been demolished by 1649.

8.4 Hooton Mill

A post mill once used to stand in the township of Hooton. Several early references to a windmill here are provided by the *Cheshire Forest Eyre Roll 1357*. The plea roll of the eyre records that a windmill, "*molendinum ventriticum*", was built in Hooton c.1345 by Henry de Hoton. The replevin roll for Wirral of 1357 also mentions Henry de Hotons's "land and his mill in Hooton". There is also a third reference to a mill in the 1357 eyre, where it is stated that twelve years previously at Hooton there was an "ancient mill", "*anticum molendinum*", this being referred to as a landmark. This mill was evidently different to that which Henry de Hoton had built c.1345, for there must have been a much older mill in the vicinity at the same time. The type of mill is not specified, so it could have been either an early windmill or a watermill. It may be recalled that in Chapter 7 the watermill of Netherpool was covered. A writer in the *Cheshire Sheaf* was quoted, who suggested that this mill may have stood on the stream which separates Overpool and Netherpool from Hooton. If a watermill did stand on this stream, which forms the Hooton township boundary, then it could be that this was the ancient mill mentioned in the eyre.

It is over two centuries until a mill is known to be mentioned at Hooton again, and this later mill may well have occupied a different site, for it was almost certainly a different structure to that built c.1345. This mill was included in the rental of Sir Rowland Stanley, which is dated 1592, and was printed in the *Cheshire Sheaf* in 1957. The rental includes reference to – "The desmesne landes in Hooton with the Parck and Mille", which were valued at £100. Eastham mill, just a short distance to the north, is also mentioned in this same rental and these two mills must have worked at the same time, very close to one another. It seems that of the Stanleys' windmills, Eastham might have ultimately entirely replaced the Hooton mill, which fell out of use some centuries earlier.

An inventory dated 1602, catalogues the possessions of James Carter, a miller in Eastham parish. I am indebted to Susan Nicholson for providing the transcription of this inventory. Along with such possessions as "old pewter dishes, a little ole saltseller and an old candlestick", the inventory includes "the tack of the Milne", the tack being the lease, which was valued at £5. It was initially assumed that James must have been the miller of Eastham mill, as he was listed within that parish. However, as can be seen in the section on that mill, the mill at Eastham was leased to Thomas Sparke, from his father's death in 1591, up until his own death in 1624. Hence, the date 1602 falls within that range, suggesting that James Carter must have held the lease of another mill in the same parish.

Confirmation of this fact came on examining James Carter's will, also dating to 1602 and held at Cheshire Record Office. The will clearly states James's occupation with the line "I James Carter of Eastham in the County of Chester miller". Later on, in the section of the will where he bequeaths his possessions is the passage – "I do leave and assigne the Lease that I have of Hooton windmill for the term of yeares in the sayd lease to come according to the true & plaine meaning therof to my sayd sonne Edward, & that my sonne John shall have the keeping of the same mill for my sayd sonne Edward towarde the keeping & maintaining of them both therwith". This fascinating passage is the only known reference which mentions Hooton windmill by name. The next item listed on the will also mentions the mill and says "I give & bequeath to Elizabeth my daughter xl s [40 shillings] & every yeare two bushels of toll corne from the sayd windemill during the terme tenn years". James Carter died in 1608 and a document exists which was signed by Edward Carter at the time of his father's death.

It is assumed that the mill continued to work up until James Carter's death and was then worked for a further period by his sons Edward and John. The mill would have had to work up until 1618 for James's daughter Elizabeth to receive the decade worth of toll corn which she was left. Unfortunately the will does not mention when the lease on the windmill expired and it is unknown if the lease was ever renewed by the Stanleys. The Carter family could have worked the mill up until its closure. There is no mention of this mill in the Stanley family account book for the period 1746-1751. Frequent references are made to both Storeton and Eastham windmills in this book – receiving rent, paying for repairs etc., thus indicating that these mills were on-going concerns. The complete lack of entries related to Hooton mill suggests that it must have fallen out of use by the mid-18th century and was no longer of financial interest.

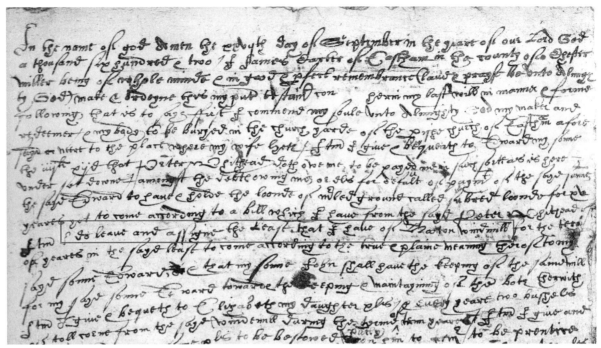

215. An extract from the will of James Carter of Eastham dated 1602. The line "I do leave and assigne the Lease that I have of Hooton windmill" has been surrounded by a box. (Courtesy of Cheshire Archives and Local Studies)

A list of all the male residents of Hooton Hall in 1743 was published by Irvine in the *Cheshire Sheaf* in November 1951. Amongst various staff, including a carpenter and labourers, there was a "Ralph Linford, miller". Certainly, one would assume that this miller must have worked one of the local windmills owned by the Stanleys. The fact that the miller was a resident of Hooton Hall suggests that he worked a mill standing reasonably close by. This gives us the possibilities of either Hooton mill or Eastham mill. In actual fact, this is probably another reference to Eastham mill, where the Stanleys' account book records a Robert Linford as the miller in 1747. The lack of any other employee given as a miller on the list could confirm that Hooton mill had fallen out of use by the 1740s. Alternatively Robert Linford could have lived at Eastham mill, in which case Ralph could have been his relative and the miller of Hooton, residing at Hooton Hall. However, the Stanleys' account book makes it clear that this mill was not in use by 1746, and there is no reason to believe it was working in 1743. It could even have fallen out of use before the turn of the 18th century.

The mill appears to be marked on the Stanley estate map, the *Township of Hooton surveyed by Charles Eyes for Sir Wm Stanley*, which was surveyed in 1776. To the west of Rivacre Road, and linked to it by a track, an enclosure is shown, in which a small circular building appears to be drawn, presumably the mill. The fields immediately surrounding the enclosure are mainly mill related in their names and there are nine "Mill Heys" in total. The Stanleys' 1825 *Map of the Manor of Hooton* lists three "Mill Heys" as field names in this vicinity, but there is no sign of the mill itself. No indication of this mill is given by Burdett in 1777, or Greenwood in 1819. In 1831 Bryant appears to mark the enclosure as a small circle, but the track linking it to Rivacre Road is not shown. The Hooton township tithe map of c.1850 shows the enclosure very clearly as a small wooded circle, within a field. To the south and west of the wooded area is a large field named "Little Mill Hey and Shires". This field seems to be formed from several smaller ones, which were shown on the Stanley estate map of 1776.

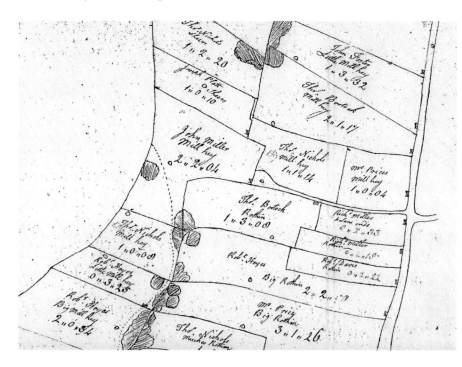

216. The 1776 Stanley estate map of Hooton township shows a circular building at the end of a track. Many mill related field names may be seen in the vicinity. (Courtesy of Cheshire Archives and Local Studies)

The mill was linked to Rivacre Road by a track which came off near to what is now called "Priory Cottage"; the tithe map marks the same building as "Keeper's Lodge". The wooded area where the mill stood continued to be marked on Ordnance Survey maps into the 20th century. It was the construction of the M53 which spelt the biggest change when it comes to the site of Hooton mill. Junction 6 of the motorway was built across Kennel Wood, leading to the utter destruction of much of the land surrounding the mill's site. The site of the former enclosure is on the south side of the motorway, just north of the eastern corner of Kennel Wood. The site itself appears undisturbed, yet it is right next to the motorway and may have been disrupted in the past. When I examined the site there was no evidence of any earthworks to indicate the location of the mill.

8.5 Little Neston Mill

Little Neston is another township where record of a windmill is ancient. Dodgson stated that the Palatinate of Chester Forest Proceedings of 1340 refer to "*molendinum de Parua Neston*", that is "the mill of Little Neston". A windmill is mentioned in numerous 17th century documents, published in the *Cheshire Sheaf* between July and September 1930, the first mention being in a deed dated 1619. It is unknown whether this later mill shared a site with the ancient mill. It may be assumed that by the 17th century the 14th century building would have undergone considerable renewals, if the site was a common one.

An indenture of settlement from 1626, published in the *Cheshire Sheaf* in July 1930, refers to "a windmill in Little Neston, a parcel of land called the Wind Milne Hill, and a hadland etc., to the said mill belonging". At this point the mill was owned by John Cottingham, who granted a share in land and property, including the mill, to people including Edward Green of Poulton Lancelyn, whose daughter Margaret was married to Charles Cottingham. The share included "half of the wind milne, and half of the profits arising therefrom, half of all reparations and charges to the said mill". So half of the profits derived from the mill were granted, but half of the cost of any necessary repair work also had to be paid. A later deed of 1683 seems to imply that the mill had been owned by a deceased Thomas Cottingham. The mill along with the "Wind Mill Hill" and other holdings were passed to another Charles Cottingham, who had a wife Elizabeth; he was listed as having use of the mill for the rest of his life in a further deed of 1711. The last manuscript printed in the *Cheshire Sheaf* to refer to the mill is a document recording a fine of 1723, again relating to one of the Cottingham family and referring to "1 windmill". The mill seems to have still been operating in 1741. This is the year in which John Davies of Little Neston died and he was described as a miller in his will, held at Cheshire Record Office.

The mill is not shown on Burdett's map surveyed from 1772-1774, and it seems that, unless it was missed, it must have disappeared in the thirty year period between 1741 and Burdett's survey. The author who published the deeds in the *Cheshire Sheaf* believed the site of this mill to be in a field named as "Mill Hill" on the Little Neston tithe map of 1849. This field lies next to a six field group variously called "Mill Field Croft" and "Mill Field Garden"; certainly such a density of mill fields points at this being the true mill site. Some of these mill fields are also marked on the Earl of Shrewsbury's estate map dated 1789. The location of the fields is south west of Windle Hill, which has sometimes been considered to derive its name from the Wind Milne Hill of the 1626 deed. In actual fact the origins of Windle were traced back much earlier by Dodgson, to "Windhul" in 1259 and "Wyndhull" in 1286. He considered that the name simply means "windy hill". The fields on the tithe map lie to the south of Lees Lane, and are now partially built upon.

8.6 Moreton Mill

Records of a windmill in Moreton may be traced back to the time when Moreton comprised part of the monastic estate of Birkenhead Priory, for this is an ancient site indeed. In the words of Stewart-Brown writing in *Birkenhead Priory and the Mersey Ferry* – "In the general account of the ecclesiastical taxation drawn up in 1291, the only estates mentioned as temporal property of Birkenhead Priory…were those in Claughton and Moreton…In Moreton…a total of £5 4s 8d from this estate including revenue from a windmill and a dovecote". A translation of the 1291 taxation itself was published in the *Cheshire Sheaf* in November 1962 and reads that "The Prior of Byrcheved…has at Morton… one wind-mill which is worth per annum ……… 12s." Brownbill in his 'A History of the Old Parish of Bidston, Cheshire', stated that "the mill and dovecot suggest that the monks regarded this estate as a separate manor". Land in Moreton may well have been given to the priory around the time of its foundation in the early 1150s.

This would have been a simple wooden mill and was clearly of ancient foundation, possibly one of the oldest sites in the area. I know of no references to this windmill after the ecclesiastical taxation, although it seems possible the mill may have lasted longer, into post-medieval times. One of the fields belonging to the Manor of Bidston and marked on the Kingston survey of 1665 is called "Milhey" and may be related to the ancient mill site. Brownbill noted this field was associated with some of the higher land in the township and thus represents a reasonable windmill site.

The Moreton township tithe map of c.1842 records two mill related field names. The fields "Mill Hay" and "Mill Moat" lie next to each other, in the south of the township, near to its boundary with Upton. "Mill Hay" appears to be the same field as that marked on the Kingston survey. Bott suggested that "Moat may be Mottre (mound), corrupted"; such earthworks are obviously a feature associated with windmill sites. These fields could feasibly show the site of the ancient windmill of Moreton, but if the ancient monastic site is forgotten they could represent a second, later site. They are not easily rationalised by many other known mill sites, although the site of the Moreton windmill could be lost and these may well be references to Upton mill, for the township boundary is very close by.

8.7 Newbold Mill

Newbold was an area in the east of Grange township, which Brownbill writing in his *West Kirby and Hilbre*, deemed to have "acquired a separate status at an early date". The Newbold estate is mentioned individually in the 1291 taxation of Pope Nicholas IV. Later on it was referred to as Newhouse or Rake House. It would seem that parts of Newbold, including the windmill there, were originally in the possession of Basingwerk Abbey. The first known reference to Newbold mill is in *Valor Ecclesiasticus*, a national survey of the wealth of the church ordered by Henry VIII in 1535. This was published by the Record Commission and Volume IV of 1821 includes a valuation of property owned by Basingwerk Abbey. Under the heading *"Villa de Newbolde"* one of the items listed is a windmill, *"moli ventritici"*, which was said to be worth 40s. per annum.

Although this is the first known reference to a windmill at Newbold, there is an earlier record of a windmill, *"molendinum ventriticum"*, at Newton cum Larton. A mill which was built c.1337 is mentioned in the eyre roll of 1357, as published by the Record Society of Lancashire and Cheshire. The eyre records that at Newton – "20 years ago the abbot of Basingwerk built in the waste there a windmill which is to the harm of the beasts, price 40s. 0d., for which the present abbot will answer and the value of the mill is half a mark a year from the time it was built…and it is to be destroyed". Although it cannot be proved, it seems highly probable that the windmill in Newton cum Larton township represented an earlier incarnation of Newbold mill. The hamlet of Newbold has sometimes been thought to comprise part of Newton cum Larton rather than Grange; for example Ormerod listed it as such in his *History* of Cheshire. Newbold is placed within Grange on the tithe map of c.1847, but is largely surrounded by land forming Newton cum Larton, and the Newbold estate contained fields in both townships. Given Basingwerk Abbey held the Newbold estate, the windmill which the abbot built in Newton cum Larton, was probably in the vicinity of Newbold.

The eyre specifies that the windmill was to be destroyed, although it is very likely that this did not happen. However, the abbot's original mill constructed c.1337 had probably been rebuilt by the time of the dissolution. So there may be the sites of two windmills at Newbold; one being the mill built during the period of the eyre, the other a later reconstruction. After the dissolution all of the abbey's property, including the mill, passed to the Crown. An Augmentation Office document of 1537, printed in *Monasticon Anglicanum*, details the belongings of the late Abbey of Basingwerk and includes a mill at "Newboll". Unlike Grange mill, this mill is not included on a list of royal mills, compiled for James I in 1608. This suggests it may have passed out of royal ownership by this date.

Brownbill's research, published in his *West Kirby and Hilbre*, showed that "On 7 January 1534/5 Nicholas, abbot of Basingwerk, granted on lease to Thomas Coventry a messuage called the Rake House and a mill called Newbold mill...". Documents relating to Basingwerk Abbey were published in the *Cheshire Sheaf* in October 1922 by J. H. E. Bennett and were written by the last abbot Nicholas Pennant in 1560. These suggest that the "windmill called Newbolde Mylne", was first let to Thomas Coyntre in the 26th year of Henry VIII's reign, or 1525. The rent for the mill was 40s. per annum and the lease was for one hundred years. By the time of the dissolution in 1536, Brownbill said that the mill was held by Thomas's son Richard Coventry and rent was payable to the Crown. In 1546 two men from Caldy Grange, one of them Richard Mylner, entered "Newbott wyndy mylne" and stole oats, barley and pease worth 10d. This record is interesting, since it shows the kind of cereals being processed at the mill in the mid-16th century.

In the late 1580s and up until 1590 a man named Robert Foster lived at New House, West Kirby and was described as a miller. Brownbill said that "In 1659 William Coventry was vouchee of...a windmill...in Newbold...In 1670 the rent of £2 13s. 4d. due to the Crown for Newbold was still charged on William Coventry; but in 1739 the trustees for the poor of West Kirby were liable for it, Edward Glegg, esq., paid 10s. for the Rakehouse, and 40s. was due from Newbold mill, but a later note in the rental says- 'No such mill or place can be found'". William Coventry had sold the Newbold estate including a windmill to Thomas Bennett in 1664. By 1676 Bennett had donated the estate to charitable usage. This is presumably how the Trustees of the Poor had become liable for it by 1739.

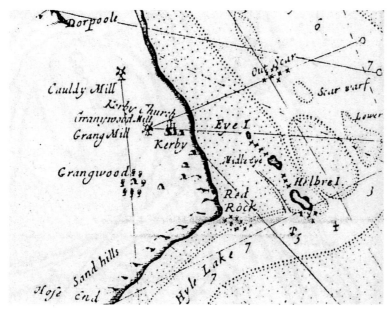

217. Collins's chart of 1689 has a drawing of a single mill at Grange. However, captions on the chart say "Granywood Mill" and "Grang Mill". Caldy mill may also be seen.

This mill must have been a post mill and seems to have disappeared at some point in the first half of the 18th century, for it was not to be found by 1739. The mill is not shown by Fearon and Eyes on their coastal survey of 1738. Intriguingly Mackay-Math's *An Abridged Plan of the River Dee and Hyle Lake*, based on a survey of 1732, marks two mills at Grange marked "Wood Mills". It could be that one of these is Newbold mill, for I know of no other strong possibilities. This could suggest that the mill disappeared between 1732 and 1736-1737, when Fearon and Eyes conducted their survey work. Although Collins drew only one mill at Grange on his 1689 survey of the River Dee, he wrote the names of two upon the chart. The more southerly of these annotations could be Newbold mill, but is labelled as "Grang Mill", the other is named "Granywood Mill". The mill latterly referred to as Grange mill, as covered in Part 2, stood in West Kirby township, whilst Newbold actually lies in Grange township.

The site of Newbold mill may still be approximated. The cluster of buildings which originally comprised Newbold is clearly identified on the c.1847 tithe map of Grange township. It is labelled "Newhouse" and the owner was the "Trustees of the Poor of West Kirby". The building which was Newhouse is now part of Oldfield Manor Farm, although it continued to be marked as "New House" on Ordnance Survey maps into the 20th century.

Directly to the south of the house, the tithe map marks a four field group of "Mill Hays". These were also owned by the Trustees of the Poor and must have originally formed part of the Newbold estate. According to Beazley, writing in the *Cheshire Sheaf* in November 1910, a reference to "Milne hey" may be found in the will of John Coventry of New House, dated 1604. Further fields which were part of the Newbold estate are found in Newton cum Larton township, the boundary of which is just west of Newhouse. Here there is a five field cluster of "Mill Hays", to the south west of Newhouse, and adjacent to those fields in Grange township. Although one cannot be conclusive, it seems probable that these fields either contain the mill site, or that the site is nearby. This would narrow down the location of the mill to a site on the southern side of Oldfield Manor Farm. None of the Mill Hay fields have been developed, so archaeological evidence may remain at this site.

8.8 Oxton Mill

A medieval windmill used to stand in Oxton township and Dodgson gave a reference to *"molendinum ventricitum"*, in the Palatinate of Chester Forest Proceedings of 1357. Dodgson was probably referring to the eyre roll of 1357, unless the forest records include another document which mentions a mill in Oxton at this date. *Cheshire Forest Eyre Roll 1357* records that in Oxton, John Donnvyll "fifteen years ago built in the waste there a windmill which is to the harm of the lord's beasts". So a windmill was built in Oxton c.1342 and still existed in 1357, although no record of it is known after this date. It is believed that a mill survived at Oxton into more recent times, yet published reference is minimal. The Earl of Shrewsbury's estate map of 1788, for his land in Oxton, shows several fields called "Mill Hey" in the south of that township, near to the boundary with Prenton.

Mitford Abraham wrote in 1903 that an "old peg mill stood at the top of Mill Hill, Oxton, but was destroyed fifty to sixty years ago. Whilst excavating below the roadway here a few years ago a large block of timber was found, which was believed to have formed part of the mill." This may well be true, and the road name Mill Hill certainly provides good evidence for Oxton mill having existed in this vicinity. However, these dates must be discarded for Mitford Abraham is referring to a mill existing into the 1840s, which seems extremely unlikely.

The Oxton township tithe map of c.1847 includes a three field group, the higher and lower "Mill Heys". These are the same fields that are shown on the 1788 Shrewsbury estate map, and they were still owned by the Earl of Shrewsbury at this point. The fields lie immediately to the south west of the Mill Hill/Holm Lane junction. The fields extend along the southern boundary of Holm Lane and one adjoins Woodchurch Road. Much of the fields now form the park to the south of Holm Lane, which may well contain the site of the mill.

This mill is not shown on Burdett's map of 1777, or any other early survey of Cheshire. Nor is it shown on the 1788 Shrewsbury estate map, which covers the area in much more detail. The mill had certainly gone by the later 18th century when the estate map was surveyed, and such is the dearth of references it probably disappeared even earlier than the 18th century.

8.9 Poulton Lancelyn Mill

An extremely early windmill is thought to have stood in Poulton Lancelyn. Several 13th century mills are known to have existed on Wirral, and some are mentioned in the ecclesiastical taxation of 1291. Earlier 13th century reference is made in an inquisition post mortem of 1284, which mentions a windmill at Storeton. Bott believed this to be the earliest mention of a windmill in the whole county of Cheshire. However, he did not consider the mill at Poulton Lancelyn, which appears to have been earlier still. The early mill at Storeton is mentioned in an inquisition into the death of Sir Philip de Bamville Knight. He was named as a witness on the charter which mentions Poulton Lancelyn mill. Hence, this inconclusively proves that the reference to a mill at Poulton Lancelyn is older.

The reference is provided by a charter in the John Rylands collection, which Irvine published in the *Cheshire Sheaf* in July 1952, and which he dated to c.1265-1270. He felt that "It cannot be earlier than 1263 as at that time Sir Roger de Domville (of Oxton) one of the witnesses had not been knighted, nor can it be later than 1279 as Philip de Bamville (of Storeton) another witness was only then knighted. The occurrence of the name of William the Welshman of Tranmere suggests that it should be dated early in this period". If this analysis is correct it makes for an early site on Wirral. One of the first definite mentions of a windmill in England is at Weedley in Yorkshire, where one was recorded in 1185, less than a century earlier.

The charter itself relates to land being granted by William de Lancelyn, to his third son Ranulph. In Irvine's English translation of the charter there is reference to a field "Winterthorn", which was described as lying "from the mill of Poulton in the direction of Storeton". Irvine said that the grantor William de Lancelyn "became Sir William in 1279 and died about 1283", further demonstrating that this reference is undoubtedly older than that to Storeton mill. The only other known reference to a mill at Poulton Lancelyn is in the plea roll of the forest eyre of 1357. This has been translated and published as *Cheshire Forest Eyre Roll 1357*. There are two instances where a mill at Poulton Lancelyn is referred to as a landmark in this roll. The first of these references states that "Richard de Pulton holds there between le Newfeld and the mill, a parcel of land called 'le Throleghfeld'". Later it was said that Richard also held "another parcel on the western side of the mill containing 3 ½ acres of land". The type of mill is not specified, but given Poulton Lancelyn windmill seems to have existed from at least 1270, it would have been a known feature of the landscape by 1357. Therefore it was probably this windmill which was being referred to.

No other references to Poulton Lancelyn windmill itself are known. Various documents seem to indirectly refer to a mill in the township, but some are references to Bromborough mill. For example, Stewart-Brown writing in the *Cheshire Sheaf* in July 1937, referred to a document of 1272. In this document, William Lancelyn of Poulton gave some land in a field to Chester Abbey, one of the boundaries of which was a ditch running "to the lepers' houses as far as Pulton Mulneway", evidently the trackway to a mill. However, this is almost certainly a reference to the road to Bromborough mill, the route referred to now probably being Spital Road. In *The Chartulary or Register of The Abbey of St. Werburgh, Chester* Irvine suggested that alternatively "There was a windmill in Poulton...so Poulton Millway may be represented by the road leading from Bebington Church to Poulton". Dodgson provided a further reference of 1343 in the John Rylands charters, at which point "*le Mulneheth*" was mentioned in the township of Poulton cum Spital. He interpreted this to mean the "heath at a mill". The location of the heath is not identified, but it seems most likely that this is an indirect reference to Poulton Lancelyn mill. Bromborough mill seems too low lying and wooded to have had any heathland nearby.

Irvine considered that "the mill of Poulton seems to have been sited on slightly rising ground to the south-west of Windy Harbour". Windy Harbour was a house to the west of Poulton Road, now demolished. The 1592 rental of Sir Rowland Stanley of Hooton, printed in the *Cheshire Sheaf* in November 1957, listed that he owned a field called "Mille ffielde" in "Pulton and Spittelle", although the location of the field is not given. This name is probably related to a field called '*le Mulnefeld*' in the 1357 forest eyre, which was held by Ranulf le Bryn, that name was also mentioned in 1343 according to Dodgson.

Additionally the estate map *A Survey And Mapp of Edward Green Esquire's Land in the Township Poolton Lancelin*, dated 1721, shows a field called "Millfield". The Poulton cum Spittal tithe map of c.1847 shows a three field group of "Mill Fields" ("Big Mill Field", "Lower Mill Field" and "Little Mill Field"), one of which is that listed on the 1721 Green estate map. The other two fields are also marked on the estate map, but are unnamed. Irvine pointed out that these fields are situated about a third of a mile from the Storeton township boundary. This fits rather well with the location of the mill mentioned in the 13th century charter and it could be that these fields represent the site. Further clues for confirming the site of the mill could come from the information provided by the 1357 eyre. It was said that "*le Throleghfeld*" lay between "le Newfeld and the mill". A field called "New Fields" on the tithe map lies a few fields away from the "Mill Fields", and may be related to "*le Newfeld*" of 1357. If the location of "*le Throleghfeld*" could also be identified, then this could help determine the site of the mill. However, the site of "*le Throleghfeld*" unfortunately remains unknown.

The tithe map "Mill Fields" have, partially at least, survived the building of large numbers of 20th century houses in this area. The remains of the fields are to the south of Old Clatterbridge Road and to the east of the motorway. Houses to the west of Poulton Royd Drive cover parts of the fields and one of these houses is called Mill Hill. A writer in the *Cheshire Sheaf* in December 1965, commenting on Irvine's 1952 postulation that the mill may have lain in these fields, said that – "his sumise was unexpectedly confirmed in 1958. My friend…when talking to Mrs. Williamson of 'Mill Hill', Poulton chanced to mention the windmill and Mrs Williamson said that when Mill Hill was built about 1920 the circular foundations of a cut-stone building were unearthed and the workmen…had remarked that this was the old windmill and that there had always been a tradition that a windmill had stood in the immediate neighbourhood".

This sounds like a most remarkable discovery, yet the note goes on to say that it went entirely unrecorded and the stones were probably reused in the building work. It seems very surprising that there would have been any local memory of a mill which appears to have disappeared so many centuries ago. If this find was indeed the foundations of a mill, then it would likely point at an age considerably more recent than the 13th or 14th century. Cheshire's earliest windmills would have been lightly built wooden structures. Stonework of a circular nature suggests a roundhouse, built around the woodwork supporting the central post of a post mill. It seems implausible that such a roundhouse could have existed at such an early date; these were not usually constructed until much later centuries.

Indeed, Paterson writing in his 'The Development of Post Mills in the NW' for the North West Mills Group stated that – "The brick or rarely stone-built roundhouse…is again difficult to date but was certainly not introduced before 1700 and appears to be confined to 1750-1850". It seems extremely unlikely that this windmill could have existed into the 18th century, for further references would surely be known. Even if a mill existed here into the 16th or 17th centuries, it would be very surprising for it to have survived entirely unrecorded, as it apparently may have done. If the remains discovered truly did represent those of a mill, then they could have provided an anomalously early date for roundhouse construction. Alternatively, some post mills may have featured short retaining walls which encompassed the mill, but did not form a full roundhouse. This kind of wall may have existed from a much earlier date than the roundhouse, and this could be what was found. However, it is certainly possible that the remains found represented a trace of another, entirely unrelated building.

8.10 Poulton Mill (including Seacombe Mill)

A windmill known as Poulton mill or Rake mill once existed in Poulton cum Seacombe township. It was a post mill which stood somewhat further south, on the same outcrop as Wallasey mill. The mill is mentioned in an inquisition post mortem of 1555 into the death of Thomas Meoles, published in the *Cheshire Sheaf* in February 1918. This makes reference to land in "a field called Pulton Feld near Le Rake Mylne in Waley". This land later passed to Thomas's son John and is said to be "near Le Rake Milne" again in an inquest held after the death of John Meoles and dated 1594. According to Harding writing in *Viking Mersey*, Le Rake Mylne simply means – "mill by the lane". Another inquisition, printed by Woods in 'The Journal of John Hough', is dated 1627 and is related to the death of William Meoles who held "land in Poulton field by Rabie Mill in Walley". This is evidently a further reference to the same land in Poulton, still held by the Meoles family. A different abstract of the same inquisition is printed in *Cheshire Inquisitions Post Mortem: Stuart Period 1603-1660*, but calls the mill "Rabia Milne".

A much earlier reference, almost certainly to this mill, is also given in 'The Journal of John Hough'. Woods referenced one of the Chester plea rolls in stating that "In 1426, Alice, widow of John de Litherland, claimed from Henry de Litherland...the Manor of Kirkby-in-Walley [Wallasey], a fourth part of the Manor of Pulton-in-Walley [Poulton], and a fourth part of the Manor of Liscark [Liscard], and 4 messuages, a mill...in these places". It is not made clear which manor the mill stood in, so this could be an early reference to any of the three post mills which stood at Wallasey, Poulton and Liscard. However, this reference is substantially earlier than the first known references to mills at either Wallasey or Liscard. That this is very likely a record of Poulton mill is shown by Booth's 'Calendar of the Cheshire Trailbaston Proceedings 1353', which was published in *Cheshire History* in 1983, and provides an even earlier reference to Poulton mill.

The trailbaston was a type of medieval court and Booth's calendar lists one hundred and thirty five different cases. Amongst these cases is an accusation that in May 1350 John Lasselles, a riding forester who was second in command to master forester William Stanley, had – "assaulted John the Miller, Henry Litherland's servant, at Poulton. Then he compelled Miller to leave Henry's service against his will, and to serve him at his own mill instead". The outcome was that John Lasselles was not guilty. This case clearly provides an indirect reference to a mill at Poulton, which was already in the hands of the Litherland family in the mid-14th century, and where John was employed by the Litherlands as a tenant miller. The Litherland family has not been discovered to have had a connection to any other mills in Wallasey and had a long association with Poulton township. Therefore the 1426 reference is surely also to Poulton mill.

This trailbaston case is also interesting in that it makes reference to John Lasselles's "own mill", where he had forced John the Miller to work. There are only two known references to this mill, and the second is another trailbaston case. Case fifty six in Booth's calendar relates that – "William Goss on Monday 1st July, 1353, forcibly entered John Lasselles's mill at Seacombe, and took away a bushel of corn". William Goss pleaded guilty and was fined 1s. 8d. The Lasselles family were the lords of Seacombe and evidently held milling rights there. The Lasselles's mill at Seacombe must have been within a few miles of the Litherland's mill at Poulton and the Poulton mill was ultimately the more long-lived, for 1353 is the last known mention of Seacombe mill. It is not known what kind of mill this was. There may once have been a stream, running through Seacombe into Wallasey Pool, although no evidence of one is known. This mill could still possibly have been a watermill, for being in Seacombe, it could have been a tide mill powered by Wallasey Pool. However, based on its seemingly short life, it is probably most likely that Seacombe mill was a medieval post mill.

The Litherlands still held the windmill at Poulton in 1558. The mill is mentioned in an inquisition post mortem into the death of Robert Litherland, dated to the 4th year of Philip and Mary's reign. In this inquisition, printed in *The Rise and Progress of Wallasey*, reference is made to seizure of "the chief messuage of Poton cu(m) Secu(m); also a…windmill and lands therein". A further inquisition dated 1636 and relating to the death of Rowland Litherland, was published in the *Cheshire Sheaf* in September 1928. On his death Rowland Litherland's lands in "Poulton with Seacombe" included "a windmill".

In the 17th century some of the Litherland family's holdings in Poulton, including the windmill, descended to the Meoles family by marriage. This is shown by the will of Thomas Meoles proved in 1663 and printed in the *Cheshire Sheaf* in June 1896. The will includes the passage "To loving wife Charlett Meoles…3rd part of rents and services out of Manor of Great Meoles and also Poulton Mill". Elsewhere the will refers to the mill as a "Wind Mill". Poulton mill is clearly shown on the Kingston survey of the Manor of Bidston dated 1665. A mill was marked in this vicinity by Collins, on his survey of the River Dee carried out in the 1680s. However, it is not possible to say if the mill marked is Poulton mill or Wallasey mill, as both mills seem to have coexisted at that time.

218. The Kingston survey marked Poulton mill in 1665, to the north of the village of "Poulton cum Seacum". (Courtesy of Cheshire Archives and Local Studies)

The Rise and Progress of Wallasey says that "Poulton or the Rake Mill, stood at the corner of Mill Lane and The Rake". The Rake no longer exists, but it was a road which stood near the junction of Mill Lane and Breck Road, which led to Poulton village. Poulton mill does not feature on any of the early surveys of Cheshire, just on the Kingston survey, which provides the last definite reference to this mill. Given its absence from Burdett's survey, it seems that this mill must have disappeared by the 1770s, and it may well have fallen out of use somewhat earlier in the 17th or 18th centuries.

What is assumed to be this mill's approximate location is recorded by the field "Mill Hay", which features on the Poulton cum Seacombe tithe map of c.1841. This field lay some way to the north of the former village of Poulton, and is now within the region enclosed by Cliff Road, Breck Road and Mill Lane. The latter road name is the most long lasting reminder of this mill, the site of which has now been entirely destroyed by urbanisation.

8.11 Puddington or Greves Mill

The plea roll which contains a record of the 1357 Wirral forest eyre contains details of various windmills, along with their approximate dates of construction. One of these references is to a windmill at "Greves", where a windmill, "*molendinum ventriticum*", was built c.1327. The eyre, as printed in *Cheshire Forest Eyre Roll 1357*, states that – "30 years ago a windmill was built in the same place [Greves] to the harm of the lord's beasts, price 40s. 0d., for which John will answer, and the value of the mill is half a mark a year, for which John will answer likewise". John was John de Leyton, who was liable for a number of fines in Greves. Greves is a lost place-name in Puddington township, the exact site of which is now uncertain. Dodgson suggested that the site of Greves may be related to the field name "Copgrave". There are three fields bearing this name on the tithe map of 1839, and these now lie alongside Pipers Lane.

The tithe map of Puddington township also shows an isolated field named "Mill Field", near to the boundary with Burton to the west of the township. In his *Notes on the Parish of Burton in Wirral*, Beazley mentioned this field and commented – "running along the ditch…is Mill Field. Before drainage took place the ditch may have been a stream sufficient for a watermill and several large ponds at its north end presenting a somewhat artificial appearance lend some colour to the conjuncture. On the other hand, fields also abutting on these ponds are called Marled field and Watering Pits. The mill may therefore have been only a gorse mill for cutting fodder". Bott felt that the same field was likely to be due to a windmill. It is generally difficult to be definitive about the origin of a single mill related field.

However, this "Mill Field" lies north of Pipers Lane, and is only a short distance from the fields "Copgrave", which adjoin that road on the southern side. This may be more than coincidental, and tends to support Dodgson's suggestion that Greves and "Copgrave" may be related. If this general area was formerly Greves, then this field is likely to have received its name from Greves windmill, the site of which might be somewhere nearby.

8.12 Shotwick Mill

There is an obscure reference which suggests that there was a windmill in Shotwick township, in addition to the watermill already mentioned. Beazley writing his 'Notes on Shotwick', detailed the inventory of the possessions of Joseph Hockenhall, who had died "in the year of our Lord God 1679". In this inventory various rooms in Shotwick Hall, for many years the residence of the Hockenhall family, are given names; one of these rooms was named as "ye miller's chamber". Even more interesting is a passage in the inventory which refers to "In ye mills...one Millhamer, two sail rodds, and a shaft, one piece of timbr eleven foot long and two over two gables and two ropes and all belonging to ye Mill £06". The reference to sail rods in particular implies that these were parts of a windmill, owned by the Hockenhalls, and extant at the time the inventory was compiled. It is likely that any local windmill owned by the Hockenhalls would have been in Shotwick, as they held that manor for over two centuries.

The field "Mill Post Hay" lies on Shotwick Brook, to the north of Shotwick watermill. One would assume that this was probably a reference to that site, although Bott felt that "'Mill Post' suggests there was also a windmill". I do not believe that this is the likely site. Alternatively, there is also a field in the township called "Two Mills Field", adjoining Parkgate Road at Two Mills and this could hold the site of the Shotwick windmill. A further group of two fields, both called "Two Mills Field", are on the opposite side of Parkgate Road, these being in Capenhurst township. The origins of the name Two Mills are confusing and have intentionally been left until Appendix A, where I have attempted to provide an unbiased examination of the potential origins of this name.

8.13 Stoak Mill

There was once a mill in Stoak township and it is believed that this was a windmill. This mill is mentioned in the 1354 rental of Sir Peter de Thornton of Thornton le Moors, which was printed in the *Cheshire Sheaf* in July 1896. One section of the rental contains a list of mills along with their annual rents. This includes the line – "The rent of the mill at Stoak annually ....xvjs. [16s.]".

The tithe map for Stoak township of c.1845 shows a three field group all called "Mill Hill", to the west of the village of Stoak. These fields seem to show a probable windmill site and they do not seem relevant to any of the other mills mentioned. It is certainly plausible that they denote the site of the mill listed in the 14th century rental. These fields lie immediately west of Junction 11 of the M53 and have probably been disturbed. In addition there are two fields, both called "Mill Field", to the north of the village of Stoak. Bott felt that these were "probably a windmill site". However, they border the Shropshire Union Canal, but a short distance west of Little Stanney mill, and I would be apprehensive about labelling them as a separate site.

8.14 Thornton Hough Mill (including Brimstage Mill)

There is a paucity of references to windmills in Thornton Hough, about which little is known. The first known record of a mill here is in the records of the 1357 forest eyre, which report that a mill, *"molendinum"*, was built in Thornton Hough c.1317 by Richard del Hough. The details of the eyre in *Cheshire Forest Eyre 1357*, state that – "Richard 40 years ago constructed there a mill in the above [mentioned in the previous plea] waste which is to the harm of the beasts, price of the mill 40s. and it is to be forfeited to the lord". The type of mill is unspecified, but it must have been a windmill for the price was 40s., and it was valued at half a mark per annum. These values are identical to those given for all other windmills built during the period of the eyre.

A windmill also stood in Thornton Hough in the 16th and 17th centuries, possibly at the same site, for it was still owned by the Hough family. In his *History* of Cheshire, Ormerod included inquisitions post mortem for the township of Thornton Hough, one of which mentions a windmill there. The enquiry of interest is into the death of William Hough in 1585, who held "the manor of Thornton Mayo, twenty messuages, one windmill, one dovecot, and two-fifths of 100 acres, called Thornton Grange". The third and last known reference to a mill at Thornton Hough is in another inquisition post mortem, this one dated 1620, and printed in *Cheshire Inquisitions Post Mortem: Stuart Period 1603-1660*. The windmill was owned by the Whitmore family at this date. Alice Hough, the only child of William Hough who was the subject of the 1585 inquisition, had married William Whitmore of Thurstaston. This second inquisition is into the deaths of William and Alice Whitmore who were "seised of fee...of the manor of Thornton Mayo & 20 messuages, a windmill, a dovecote...& 2 parts of 100 acres of lands in 5 parts divided called Thornton Grange".

There are two significant groups of mill related fields on the 1847 tithe map of Thornton Hough township. The first group is to the south of the township, at the boundary with Great Neston. Here there are six fields called variously "Mill Hey" and "Mill Brow". These fields do not seem relevant to any other site mentioned. Such a large group of fields seems likely to show a true mill site and it is felt that these must relate to the windmill of the 1585 and 1620 inquisitions. These fields lie either side of Liverpool Road, south of Parkgate Lane. They are partially built upon, but much land in their vicinity remains undeveloped and the site of this mill could remain undisturbed.

To the north of Thornton Hough, Bryant's map of 1831 marks what is now Manor Road, as "Mill Ho. Lane". Some way up that road and probably in Brimstage township, a building is labelled "Mill Ho. or Thatched Hall". Another significant group of mill fields on the tithe map lies to the north of Thornton Hough and comprises a five field group either side of Manor Road. These fields are all called "Mill Hey", adjoin the Brimstage township boundary and are clearly related to the features marked on Bryant's map. As mentioned in the section on Brimstage watermill, a windmill is said to have existed in Brimstage. I know of no primary references to the Brimstage windmill, but it is felt that these fields suggest its probable location, given they are so close to the boundary with Brimstage. Some of these fields are now partially covered by Thornton Manor; others are to the east of Thornton Manor, south of Talbot Avenue and have not been built on. Local archaeologist Peter France has suggested that Brimstage windmill stood near to the footpath at the top of Talbot Avenue.

219. Bryant labelled what is now Manor Road as "Mill Ho. Lane" and this name may commemorate a windmill in Brimstage township.

8.15 Upton Mill

References to a windmill in Upton are scarce. The first known mention was furnished by Ormerod in his *History* of Cheshire. Mention is made of Laurence Bold who held the manor of Upton from Elizabeth I and died in 1567. He was married to Margery Glegg of Gayton and in 1557 William Glegg obtained from him by fine, "the manor of Upton... one mill and 27000 acres of various kinds of land in Upton, Frankby and Arrow". The mill was still a possession of the Bold family in the early 17th century, at which point it was referred to in two inquisitions post mortem. The first of these inquisitions is dated 1614 and relates to the death of Peter Bold of Upton, the nephew of the Laurence Bold who died in 1567. The second inquisition is dated 1619 and is an enquiry into Henry Bold's death. Both inquisitions were printed in *Cheshire Inquisitions Post Mortem: Stuart Period 1603-1660*, they mention the seizure of the manor of Upton including the windmill. For example, the inquisition relating to Henry Bold states that – "before his death the said Henry was seised in fee of the manor of Upton & of a capital mess[uage] called the Hall of Upton & of 9 mess[uages], a windmill".

The final known mentions of this mill come in the 'Sequestrators' Accounts for Wirral', published in the *Cheshire Sheaf* in 1956. A mill is listed at Upton under the rents paid to the Earl of Derby, alongside those which were paid for Bidston mill. The accounts for December 1644 list that the Earl received £1 10s. from "John Woofall for Upton Mill", which constituted a quarter year's rent. In 1646 James Woofall is recorded to have paid £4 10s. for "the Milne at Upton". The windmill at Upton was then catalogued in a list of the Lord Derby's possessions dated 1647, and this is the last known record of this mill, although it seems likely that further unpublished references may remain, certainly for a mill which survived into the 17th century.

According to the *Cheshire Sheaf* of July 1953 a field called "Mill Moote" existed in Upton in 1726, when Sir Rowland Stanley leased it to Arthur Bennett. This could be related to the field "Mill Moat" on the Moreton township tithe map. The Upton township tithe map of c.1839 shows a group of three mill fields, including the names "Mill Hay" and "Mill Wheat". These fields lie to the east of Saughall Massie village, on either side of Saughall Massie Road. Another related field, just to the west of this group, is "Mill Looms" which lies in Saughall Massie township. These fields are not a great distance from Saughall Massie mill. However, in this instance they seem far enough removed to indicate a distinct site and they could well denote the approximate location of Upton mill. This seems the most probable site, but there is also a chance that the field names mentioned in association with Moreton mill show the site of Upton mill, for they adjoin the boundary with Upton township. Both sets of fields have now been built upon.

PART 4: OUTSTANDING MILLS AND APPENDICES

CHAPTER 9: ADDITIONAL MILLING SITES

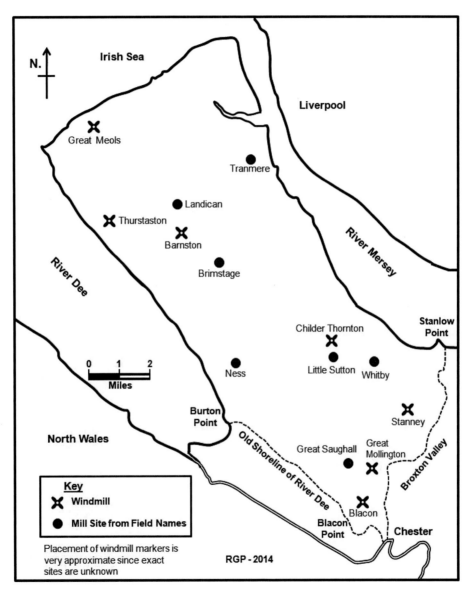

220. The additional milling sites supported by primary references or by field names and covered in Part 4, Chapter 9.

This book has hopefully shown that for an area of land of some one hundred square miles, the number of mill sites scattered around the Wirral Peninsula is fairly large. The mills I have written of so far are those backed up by documentary evidence. Most in Part 2 are well supported by an array of historic documentation. For those in Part 3 there are often more limited references, sometimes just one. However, further sites must surely exist, where no known documentary sources are present. References to mills in ancient documents are often incidental and unrecorded sites are likely to exist, especially for windmills which may have been used for only a short period of time. Some such sites may have already been mentioned, especially in Part 3, where for convenience an unsupported site of little standing may have been briefly noted as an aside to the main section. The main sites included in this manner within Part 3 are windmills at Brimstage and Whitby, and watermills at Tranmere and Shotwick Castle. The castle mill seems somewhat unfounded, but the other sites are potentially more plausible.

There are a few further sites which have not been mentioned and so as to round things off these have been placed in this final chapter. Some of these sites rely on field name evidence alone and more sites of this nature probably exist. However, it is felt that any of real consequence have been mentioned here. It is extremely difficult to say how many unrecorded sites could exist. Groups of mill related fields tend to suggest a true site, whereas isolated fields with mill related names are less convincing. An examination of field names on tithe maps of Wirral will show many mill related field names, some at locations where no known records exist. It is impossible to vouch for the origins of such field names, yet it seems probable that some show forgotten milling sites. A mill standing nearby is the most likely explanation for how these fields acquired their names, since names were often based on prominent local features. Primary references could exist which would prove the presence of mills at some of these locations.

As well as further sites identified by field names, there are also a number of mills for which primary references are known. Despite being supported by primary references, these mills could not warrant a section in Part 3, since their sites within the township are unknown. A likely site was suggested for all mills in Part 3, but for these mills there is no suitable field name evidence to suggest potential sites. In addition there are some sites which are mentioned in secondary sources, but I have found no proof that they are true locations. This chapter is split into two sub-sections; first the mills are covered which are mentioned in primary and secondary references, then the sites suggested by field names are discussed.

9.1 Further Mills from Primary and Secondary References

Mention has already been made, in the introduction to Part 3, of windmills which were built in the period of the 1357 eyre, and these were described in the eyre plea roll. These mills had been constructed unlawfully with respect to forest laws, and a fine had yet to be paid. They were probably never demolished even though the eyre consistently stated they should be. Many windmills covered by the eyre have already been written of in Chapter 8. However, the *Cheshire Forest Eyre Roll 1357* refers to a number of these mills at locations where no other references have been found. All of these remaining mills are specifically said to be windmills, for the Latin transcription calls them *"molendinum ventriticum"*. It has not been possible to identify a likely site for any of these mills, so they will be described together in this chapter. The pleas relating to each mill are very similar and often repeat common information, so they will not necessarily be quoted in full.

There was once a windmill in Blacon cum Crabwell township, just within the boundaries of the Hundred of Wirral. This windmill is mentioned twice in the plea roll associated with the 1357 eyre. The first reference gives the mill as a landmark c.1327. It was said that William Trussell had "30 years ago assarted there in the waste next to the windmill 24 ½ acres 32 ½ perches of land". The term "assart" meant the clearing of previously unfarmed land, to bring it under cultivation. This was a finable offence. Another fine for which William Trussell was accountable, was for the construction of a windmill at Blacon c.1337, and this mill still existed in 1357. Apparently William had "20 years ago built in the waste there a windmill". This indicates that there were actually two windmills in Blacon around this time. One certainly still existed in 1357 and had been built approximately 1337. Clearly, this cannot be the same mill which had existed at Blacon thirty years earlier c.1327. However, nothing specific has been discovered about the locations of Blacon's windmills, for unfortunately the tithe map of the township lists no field names of value to this study.

All of the remaining windmills are mentioned just once within the eyre. The first of these mills to have been built was at Thurstaston, and had been built by John Dourne c.1327. The plea roll states that – "John 30 years ago built in the waste there a windmill which is to the harm of the beasts, price 40s. 0d., for which John will answer and it is to be destroyed". There is certainly high ground which would be suitable for a windmill in this township, but there are no relevant field names to indicate the possible site, which remains unknown.

A similar case is presented by a windmill at Great Mollington. This had been built "in the waste" of the township c.1337 by John de Ruyton and William Toraud. As usual, it was emphasised that the mill should be "pulled down and destroyed". Despite the fact that this probably never happened, the windmill at Great Mollington does not seem to have been especially long-lived, as no other references to it are known. No instances of mill related field names have been discovered in this township. However, a large group of ten fields named "Mill Field" lie in Great Saughall township, the origins of which are unknown. These are covered in the second part of this chapter and are near to the boundary with Great Mollington, so there is a chance that they are related to the site of this mill.

Windmills built under twenty years before the eyre seem to have been given a more accurate date of construction, not one simply rounded to the nearest decade. At Stanney for example "Richard sixteen years ago erected there in the waste seven messuages and a windmill which are to the harm of the beasts; the price of each messuage is 40d. and that of the mill is 40s. 0d., for which Richard will answer and they are to be forfeit and destroyed; and the value of the mill is half a mark a year from the time it was built, and of each messuage 12d., for which Richard will answer likewise." Richard was Richard de Bunbury, lord of Stanney. Once again, the site of this windmill is not known.

The last of these little recorded windmills is said to have stood in Barnston, and was built c.1345, for it had been built "twelve years ago" in 1357. It was constructed by Robert de Barnston, who had built the mill in the waste of the township. Nothing else has been discovered about this windmill, which was built before the first known reference to Barnston watermill in 1376. All of the windmills just described were working at the time of the eyre, for they were all valued at half a mark per year, from the time they were built, up until 1357. However, the eyre provides the only known reference to all of these mills and nothing is known about any of them after 1357.

Brownbill stated in *West Kirby and Hilbre* that there was formerly a mill in the township of Great Meols. He referred to an inquisition post mortem of 1349, into the death of Henry de Meles, possibly a victim of the Black Death. The Black Death caused such a significant decrease in the population that there was a related decrease in the number of operational mills across the country. The inquisition states that Henry de Meles held a windmill within his estate of Great Meols. Another reference is in a second inquisition post mortem of 1350; this was printed by Ormerod in his *History* of Cheshire. The inquisition is into the death of "Bertram de Meeles" who "held the manor of Meeles...and one windmill worth x11d. Per annum". These mentions are doubtless true, but I know of no field names to show the potential site. The second inquisition is also mentioned by Sulley in his *The Hundred of Wirral*. He wrote of the ancient manor house of Meols, once situated on Dove Point, but subsequently washed away, and suggested that any windmill "has also long succumbed to the ravages of the sea". So it could be that the land on which this windmill stood has now been entirely lost.

A similar scenario presents itself in the township of Childer Thornton. A single reference is known to a mill in this township, which it is assumed must have been a post mill. E. M. Hance provided a paper on 'Notes on the ancient Cheshire families of Bennett of Saughall Massey and Bennett of Barnston, with their collateral branches', printed in the *Transactions of the Historic Society of Lancashire and Cheshire* for 1886. Hance referenced a will dated 1690 for Thomas Bennett of Childer Thornton, who died in 1691. This will records that "the residue of his [Thomas Bennett's] estate, including his mill at Childer-Thornton and his lands at Liscart [Liscard] he devised...to his grandson Thomas Young". This will provides the only known record of a mill at Childer Thornton and is also dated relatively late for a structure which has yielded no other references. However, the source is seemingly unambiguous, clearly stating that the mill stood in Childer Thornton, a relatively small township. This mill was evidently held by the Bennett family and does not seem to be synonymous with any other nearby mill. There are no useful field names in Childer Thornton to indicate any likely site. However, there are two mill related fields in the adjoining township of Little Sutton and these may commemorate this mill, as mentioned in the second part of this chapter.

Writing in *Twixt Mersey and Dee*, Gamlin made passing mention of a gorse mill upon Bidston Hill, unconnected to the familiar flour mill there. Gorse mills were used specifically to crush gorse, to produce cattle and horse feed. I can find little further information on this one. Mitford Abraham stated that "The site of this structure is not known, and it seems to have been destroyed at least a century ago". Brownbill made some further reference in his 'A History of the Old Parish of Bidston, Cheshire', commenting on gorse being beaten by hand until the construction of a gorse mill. The motive power for this mill is not known and it could even have been a horse mill.

Mitford Abraham mentioned an ancient windmill having once stood in Noctorum, although I know of no other mention and this statement seems to be incorrect. I have also seen mention of a post-medieval windmill in Prenton, in addition to the Domesday watermill there. This is suggested in documentation associated with the Merseyside Historic Environment Record. I have been unable to verify this claim and there are no field names on the tithe map to help suggest a probable site.

9.2 Further Mills from Field Name Evidence

There are three fields in Grange called "Mill Hay"; these form an isolated group, some way from the well known mill site covered in Part 2. Bott felt that this was a definite additional windmill site, now built upon. I would be a little more tentative about suggesting this. The mill mentioned in Part 2 is so well documented that one wonders how a second mill could have escaped any documentary mention, unless Grange mill was perhaps resited at some point. As mentioned previously, John Mackay-Math's 1732 plan of the River Dee marks two mills at Grange and Collins's survey of 1689 appears to do so too. It was suggested in Part 3 that one of these was probably Newbold mill. However, as an alternative, these charts could provide support for an otherwise unrecorded mill at this site.

A three field group, all called "Mill Field", lie in Landican township, to the south west of the village and at the boundary with Arrowe and Thingwall townships. This location has been stated to show the probable site of a windmill by Bott and others, but no known documentary evidence exists. What remains of these fields is south of Landican Cemetery, between Landican Road and Arrowe Park Road.

There is believed to have been at least one windmill in Ness. The primary site is to the east of the village, south of Mill Lane and in the vicinity of Flashes Lane. The majority of mill related road names are associated with mills of which much more evidence remains. The perpetuation of Mill Lane, which seemingly commemorates this unrecorded site, is interesting. This road name was recorded on Bryant's map of 1831, but the mill itself must have disappeared long before. The tithe map of c.1845 marks a four field group all called "Mill Hill", and it is felt that these must relate to the windmill site from which Mill Lane derives its name; the age is unknown.

There are also a couple of isolated field names in Ness, applying to just a single field. Bott felt that "Miller's Croft", to the west of the village, was a "probable windmill site on land now occupied by a housing estate". Another isolated field is "Miller's Stud Fold", which Bott thought "may indicate a windmill site north-east of Haddon Hall Farm". One has to be especially wary of fields with "Miller's" in the name, for they may simply indicate former land ownership by a miller, nowhere near the mill in question. These fields have much less claim to a true mill site than those on Mill Lane, which certainly purport to be a genuine one.

The Little Sutton township tithe map of c.1848 marks two fields called "Mill Field" and "Lower Mill Field" next to Sutton Hall and to the north of Ledsham Road. These may well preserve a windmill site, now built upon. The fields lay just south of Margaret's Lane and adjoined the boundary with Childer Thornton township to the north. There is a chance that these fields may be related to the windmill which was recorded at Childer Thornton in 1690, as mentioned in the first part of this chapter. If so, this windmill may have stood somewhere to the north, in the southern part of Childer Thornton.

In Great Saughall township there is a very large group of ten "Mill Fields" ("Mill Field", "Big Mill Field", "Far Mill Field", etc.), to the west of Parkgate Road. These are a considerable distance south of the Gibbet mill and seemingly unrelated to it. So many mill fields must surely be related to another mill site, probably a windmill. Commenting on these fields Bott felt that – "A small brook…makes a watermill site just possible, but a windmill is more likely". The only known windmill which could have stood near these fields is the one at Great Mollington, covered in the first part of this chapter. This was built c.1337, during the period of the 1357 eyre. These "Mill Fields" are very near to the boundary of Great Mollington, so there is a chance they could commemorate the site of the windmill in that township.

APPENDIX A: THE ORIGINS OF THE NAME TWO MILLS

Two Mills is a hamlet situated on Parkgate Road, a cluster of buildings, lying about the junctions of that road with Chapel Lane and Capenhurst Lane. Its name is evidently derived from two mills of some kind; however, there appears to be a long standing confusion as to what these mills were. I have deliberately not related this name to any of the sites given earlier on. It seemed prudent to discuss all sites first, irrespective of this name, the origins of which have been included within this appendix.

The earliest known reference to the name Two Mills is in the 1668 survey of Wirral made by Randle Holme III, the famous Cheshire heraldry painter. His survey, now preserved amongst the Harleian Manuscripts, was reproduced in the Appendix to Mortimer's *The History of the Hundred of Wirral*. The survey lists the towns of Wirral in 1668, along with notes on the lords of those towns. Also given are comments on "Hamlets and places of note"; these mention hamlets near to the towns in question, or significant buildings, such as ancient halls. Randle Holme III referred to "Two milnes on ye heath", as a hamlet or place of note associated with Shotwick. He would doubtless have thought there was nothing particularly notable about two actual mills, and so the reference is obviously as the place-name of a hamlet.

Further references occur throughout the 18th century. One example is a marriage listed in the parish registers of St. Mary's, Chester, in 1740, which was published in the *Cheshire Sheaf* in January 1883. Here the bride, Mary Francis, is listed as being "of ye 2 Mills of ye Heath". In the details of an execution printed in the *Chester Courant* of 1750, already quoted in the section on the Gibbet mill, executed murderers were said to be gibbeted near "the Two Mills on the Heath". This sounds like a reference to two physical mill buildings, but it is assumed to be a place-name as for the previous examples. The 1763 will of Samuel Bennett of Shotwick, printed in the *Cheshire Sheaf* in January 1921, refers to a farm he hoped to build – "between the mill dam and the Two Mills on the Heath". This is the dam of Puddington mill, and suggests that it remained a recognised feature long after that mill itself had ceased to work.

These references are confusing since in all instances it sounds rather like two extant mill buildings, present at that point, are being mentioned. However, The Two Mills of/on The Heath was obviously actually a place-name, later shortened simply to Two Mills. Even in Randle Holme III's time, the actual existence of any working mills is uncertain. In 1668 the hamlet evidently already had the name Two Mills on the Heath, and its namesake may have disappeared by this time. Burdett marked the present day hamlet of Two Mills as "Mills Heath" on his map of 1777, a name also used on Smith's *Map of Wirral and Chester* dated 1808. The hamlet had adopted the current name of Two Mills on Greenwood's map of 1819, and is also marked as such on Bryant's map of 1831.

Mitford Abraham stated in 1903 that "on the Parkgate Road, is an inn called 'The Yacht', round which is a collection of small houses abutting on the road, the whole going under the name of 'Two Mills'. Formerly there stood nearly opposite the inn two windmills, both of which were destroyed sixty to seventy years ago. The sign on the inn used to be a painting of these two mills, and some residents in the neighbourhood still remember this old signboard". It is doubtless untrue that any windmills remained here into the 1830s and The Yacht Inn is actually in the hamlet of Woodbank, just south of Two Mills. However, the former name of the inn would seem to be true, for a list of ale sellers dated 1822 lists pubs called "Two Mills" in both Woodbank and Capenhurst, that at Capenhurst also being marked on Bryant's map of 1831. In reference to the inn at Woodbank, Bott quoted the activities of a highwayman mentioned in the *Chester Courant* of 10th June 1760, which states "the postilion rode on to the Sign of the Two Windmills", showing this to be a pub name of at least 18th century origin.

Mitford Abraham's belief that two windmills stood in this vicinity is discredited in the *Cheshire Sheaf,* in which it is stated multiple times that the two mills referred to must be watermills. For example in February 1921 – "there are still to be seen on Shotwick Brook the remains of two mill-dams which show that two mills must have been water-mills". This belief is also expressed by Norris in his survey of Cheshire watermills. The mills referred to are the watermills of Puddington and Shotwick, covered in detail in Part 3. However, I know of no mention of either of these mills after the 14th century and since they stood within the little gorge carved by Shotwick Brook, they certainly could not be described to stand on the heath, nor would they have been especially visible. Puddington mill may have stood near Parkgate Road, but was considerably to the north of the hamlet of Two Mills. Shotwick mill stood hidden deep in Shotwick Dale, a significant distance south west of Two Mills and could not possibly have been seen from Parkgate Road. These points surely cast doubt on previous beliefs that these watermills gave the hamlet its name.

However, there may be more truth than is generally realised in Mitford Abraham's comments. It may be recalled from Part 3 that a windmill was mentioned at Capenhurst in 1357, 1517 and 1597. The proposed site, identified through field name evidence, lies a little way to the north east of Two Mills, in an area which may well have once been heathland. The heath where this windmill stood is believed to have been Ledsham Heath, also named Motherless Heath on a plea roll of 1543. It was also called "a great spacious common, which they vulgarly called Motherless Heath", by William Webb in his 1621 'Itinerary of Wirral Hundred', which was reprinted by Ormerod. This is identifiable as the Mills Heath of Burdett's map. There is a paucity of information on the Capenhurst windmill and there is no reason to doubt that, at one point, a second windmill could also have stood there on the same piece of heathland.

It was also mentioned in Part 3 that a windmill at Shotwick was mentioned in Joseph Hockenhall's inventory of 1679. Attention was drawn to a field named "Two Mills Field" on the Shotwick township tithe map of c.1848. This lies at Two Mills, on the west side of Parkgate Road, opposite Chapel Lane and could be the site of the Shotwick windmill. Even if this particular field is not the site of Shotwick's windmill, it is likely that it stood in this vicinity. If so, windmills could have stood on either side of Parkgate Road in Shotwick and Capenhurst and at least one, but easily both, could even have existed when Randle Holme III mentioned the area in 1668. Certainly the existence of windmills would fit the description of Two Mills of/on the Heath much better than any evidence provided by watermills. It also seems highly likely given the former inn name, "Two Windmills", which was evidently of early foundation.

Bott also believed that windmills gave this hamlet its name. He seemed to feel that two windmills could have stood on a further group of two mill related fields, both called "Two Mills Field". These are in Capenhurst township; shown on the tithe map of 1840, they are enclosed by Capenhurst Lane and at a position directly opposite The Yacht Inn. However, fields of this name could very easily be so named due to their presence near Two Mills hamlet. There is nothing to date them, or substantiate their namesake with a true mill site. I believe that in addition to the two watermills, which are not relevant to this place-name, there were probably at least two windmills, one in Shotwick and one in Capenhurst. These seem likely to have given the hamlet its name. There was possibly a third windmill at some point, also in Capenhurst township, but the field name evidence cannot be relied upon.

Bott believed that "There were almost certainly five, and probably seven, cornmills within ¾ of a mile of Two Mills". This is an extremely generous analysis and I would say there were probably four mills in this area, two watermills and two windmills, and possibly a third windmill. That is not including the more recent Gibbet mill, which stands somewhat further south. The important point is that it seems highly likely that it was in fact two windmills, not two watermills, which gave this hamlet its name.

APPENDIX B: A SUMMARY OF WIRRAL'S MILLS

The information contained throughout this book has been summarised within this second appendix. The facts are presented in several tables, which give a range of important dates, concerning the existence of each mill. One table refers to the mills covered in Part 2, whilst those listed in Part 3 occupy a second table. Two more tables refer to the mills mentioned earlier in Part 4. All mills supported by primary references are numbered, whilst unsubstantiated mills contained within Parts 3 and 4 have been assigned a letter. These unsubstantiated mills primarily represent the more likely sites, often those which are supported by strong field name evidence. Some additional sites within Part 4, Chapter 9 were discounted from inclusion within the table.

The "First Known Record" column is a judge of the antiquity of each site, based upon when a mill is first known to have been mentioned there. The word "known" is of course inserted intentionally, for many mills will predate the first reference given, and it may well be that earlier references exist. Other columns show the dates for the last use of each mill and dates of demolition, or house conversion. It must be stressed that these tables provide only a general overview. Some of the construction dates and dates of last use are reasonable estimates, based on available facts. They cannot be vouched for, but as assumptions seem fairly accurate. In some cases the true date of an event is unknown and an estimate could not be satisfactorily deduced; in these cases there is a dash in that box. The table for Part 3 is necessarily vaguer than that for Part 2, due to the little recorded nature of many of these sites. Sources for all of the dates, and explanations for any notes within the boxes, are covered in further detail within the relevant sections. Those sections must remain the first point of reference, but it is hoped that these tables will provide a useful resource for drawing comparisons between sites.

Table 1: A summary of the mills covered in Part 2.

No.	Mill	Type of Mill	First Known Record	Last Worked	Final Fate
1	Liscard	Post	1754	Early 1830s	Demolished c.1833
2	Wallasey	Post	1665	Replaced 1765	Demolished
3	Wallasey	3 Storey Tower	Built 1765	Early 1880s	Demolished 1887

4	Saughall Massie	Post	1598	Early 1860s	Demolished early 1870s
5	Wallasey Pool (two individual mills)	Water/Tide (Undershot?)	1745	c.1806	Demolished by 1819
6	Bidston Thwaite (multiple mills)	Post	1357 (Built 1352 or 1353)	Pre-1596	Demolished
7	Bidston	Post	1596	1791	Destroyed by fire 1791
8	Bidston	3 Storey Tower	Built c.1800	c.1875	Restored 1894
9	Grange	Post	1535	1839	Destroyed by gale 1839
10	Irby (ancient site, multiple mills)	Post	1291	Replaced early 1700s	Demolished
11	Irby (later site)	Post	Built 1709-1725	Later 1880s	Demolished 1898
12	Thingwall	Assumed Post (possibly also early tower)	1650	Replaced 1866	Demolished
13	Thingwall	4 Storey Tower	Built 1866	1897	Demolished 1900
14	Heswall	Post	1357 (Built c.1327)	-	Demolished
15	Gayton	3 Storey Tower	Built c.1735	Later 1870s	House Conversion 1990
16	Neston (Raby Park Road)	Post	1596	Pre-1772-1774	Demolished by 1811
17	Neston	Assumed Post	Built 1729	1820s or 1830s (possibly 1822)	Destroyed by gale
18	Neston	3 Storey Tower	Built 1732-1774	c.1885	Commercial Premises by 1960s; House from c.1990
19	Tranmere (also an ancient site)	5 Storey Tower	Built 1790s	1850s or early 1860s	Demolished early 1870s

20	Storeton (multiple mills)	Post	1284	Replaced 1810s	Demolished
21	Higher Bebington	Post	1424	-	Demolished
22	Higher Bebington	4 Storey Tower	Built c.1810s	c.1901	Demolished 1968
23	Bromborough (multiple reconstructions)	Water/Tide (Undershot)	1086 (last mill 18th century)	1910 (by water) 1940 (by oil engine)	Demolished 1949
24	Bromborough	4 Storey Tower	Built 1777	Later 1860s	Demolished 1878
25	Raby (multiple reconstructions)	Water (Overshot)	1398 (present ruin 17th century)	Later 1880s	Ruins remain (partially demolished 1910s)
26	Eastham	Post	1591	Replaced 1740s-1750s	Demolished
27	Eastham	3 Storey Tower	Built early 1740s or 1750s	Mid-1890s	Demolished 1940
28	Willaston (multiple mills)	Post	1321	Replaced c.1800	Demolished
29	Willaston	5 Storey Tower	Built c.1800	1930 (powered by wind/gas engine)	House Conversion 1958
30	Burton/Denhall (ancient site)	Post	1315	Replaced 1629 or early 1700s	Demolished
31	Burton (later site)	Post	1629 or early 1700s (present ruin 18th century)	Either late 1870s or c.1882	Ruins remain (partially demolished 1890s)
32	Little Stanney (multiple reconstructions)	Water (Undershot)	Pre-1184 (last mill rebuilt 1820s)	1906-1910	Demolished later 1940s
33	Great Stanney or Flyndal	Water	Pre-1190	1279 (?)	Demolished
34	Great Saughall or Gibbet	3 Storey Tower	Built c.1774	1926	House Conversion 1971

Table 2: A summary of the mills covered in Part 3.

No.	Mill	Type of Mill	First Known Record	Last Known Record	Last Worked/ Notes
35	Arrowe	Water	1347	1347	-
36	Barnston	Water (Undershot?)	1376	1376	Stonework present
37	Birkenhead Priory	Water(/Tide?)	1291	1647	1647?
38	Brimstage	Water	1278	1278	-
39	Netherpool (multiple sites?)	Water	1308	1402	-
40	Prenton	Water	1086	1608	Pre-18th Century?
41	Puddington	Water	1357	1369	-
42	Shotwick	Water (Undershot?)	1302	1302	Stonework present
43	Storeton	Water	1284	1295	Pre-1349, Culvert present
44	Backford	Post	1597	1649	Pre-1649
45	Caldy (multiple sites?)	Post	1553 (1454 indirectly)	1766 (different site?)	Later 18th century
46	Capenhurst (multiple sites?)	Post	1357 (Built c.1336)	1597	-
47	Chorlton	Post	1392	1398	-
48	Hooton (multiple sites?)	Post	1357 (Built c.1345)	1608	Pre-1746
49	Little Neston (multiple sites?)	Post	1340	1741	Pre-1774
50	Moreton	Post	1291	1291	Pre-1665
51	Newbold/Newton cum Larton (multiple sites?)	Post	1357 (Built c.1337)	1739	Pre-1739
52	Oxton	Post	1357 (Built c.1342)	1357	-
53	Poulton Lancelyn	Post	c.1265-1270	1357	-
54	Poulton	Post	1350	1665	Pre-1774

55	Puddington (Greves)	Post	1357 (Built c.1327)	1357	-
56	Seacombe	Post	1350	1353	-
57	Shotwick	Post	1679	1679	Pre-18th Century?
58	Stoak	Post	1354	1354	-
59	Thornton Hough (multiple sites?)	Post	1357 (Built c.1317)	1620	-
60	Upton	Post	1357	1646	Pre-18th Century?

Table 3: A summary of the mills covered in Part 4, Chapter 9.1.

No.	Township	Dates	Mill Type
61	Barnston	1357 (Built c.1345)	Post
62	Blacon cum Crabwell (two sites)	1357 (Extant c.1327 and built c.1337)	Post
63	Childer Thornton	1691	Post
64	Great Meols	1349 and 1350	Post
65	Great Mollington	1357 (Built c.1337)	Post
66	Stanney	1357 (Built c.1341)	Post
67	Thurstaston	1357 (Built c.1337)	Post

Table 4: A select summary of the probable mill sites covered in Parts 3 and 4

Letter	Township	Evidence	Proposed Mill Type
A	Brimstage	Field names only	Post
B	Great Saughall	Field names only (related to No. 65?)	Post/Water
C	Landican	Field names only	Post
D	Little Sutton	Field names only (related to No.63?)	Post
E	Ness	Field names only	Post
F	Prenton	Merseyside Historic Environment Record	Post
G	Tranmere	Field names only	Water
H	Whitby	Field names only	Post

CONCLUDING THOUGHTS

I have extensively researched the sites and histories of Wirral's windmills and watermills over many years. Any historical account must build upon the work of previous historians and this book has compiled many other people's research, along with my own. We owe a huge debt to all of the local historians who have recorded Wirral's past, especially now that all traces of so many mills have been entirely lost. This survey aims to be comprehensive and I believe that the vast majority of mill sites on the peninsula, to have existed since the Domesday survey, must have been covered. Unrecorded Anglo-Saxon or even Roman sites which had stopped working before the Norman Conquest and were not listed in the Domesday Book could remain, but such sites would be very rare.

Certainly all sites to have existed from the later 18th century onwards are included, and hopefully the majority of additional sites recorded between Domesday and Burdett's survey are also covered. That has been my aim and to my knowledge there are no outstanding sites. However, I cannot proclaim that this is an exhaustive work, for such a claim can never truly be made and there are certainly outstanding sources which I have been unable to consult. New information will doubtless come to light, for there is still primary documentation which could be examined, and further research into Wirral's mills is strongly encouraged. There are original documents, transcriptions of which have never been published, and these could well refer to ancient mills, which I have failed to include. I feel that all sites of historic significance are likely covered, but there could be minor, short-lived sites, which remain unidentified. I hope that this book will prove helpful to fellow students of local history. It is accurate to the best of my knowledge and if it is of any use to others then it has served its purpose admirably.

The finished piece of work contains detailed individual sections covering some forty three mills. However, Appendix B shows that the number of mills covered is in fact more like sixty seven. A further eight probable mill sites are identified via field names, mainly in the second part of Chapter 9, and a quantity of less promising sites are also included. Where possible, as well as attempting to provide a detailed history of each mill from transcriptions of original sources, I have also included a photographic history of the existence of Wirral's mills and maps of their localities. This was successfully achieved for Part 2, but proved less feasible for Part 3, where many sites are of great antiquity. Still, the elusive nature of most of the milling sites in Part 3 is such that they have rarely, if ever, been written of before. In this work, possible locations have been postulated for all of these ancient mills. Possible sites could not be identified for the medieval mills included in the first part of Chapter 9, but these are minor and ancient sites, some of which have never been written about before.

A detailed account on this scale, covering the many milling sites on Wirral, has never been attempted before. This book hopefully corrects the fact that a thorough history of Wirral's mills has been omitted from the local literature for so long. This completed book attempts to cover every windmill and watermill site recorded to have existed within the boundaries of the Hundred of Wirral, from the Norman period, until traditional milling ceased in the 20th century. As such, it encompasses many centuries of history, over the course of which social and technological developments have been profound. Yet, the venerable craft of traditional milling remained remarkably unchanged over this same time period.

My main aim was to find out what traces remain of an industry which has now all but disappeared in this area. Our ancestors harnessed the natural powers of wind and water to grind their cereals, a practice that has entirely vanished with the march of commercial progress. I was pleasantly surprised, for although the first cursory glance will show so many of Wirral's mills to be demolished, even the most unlikely site holds evidence in many cases. It is undeniable that some of the sites I visited held virtually no remains. However, a good selection of buildings and ruins remain, to remind us how things were in an area rich with milling history. Let us hope that the destruction of Wirral's mills is now at an end. The milling industry, a crucial component of any traditional rural economy, has left its mark on Wirral's landscape, and these sites deserve to be remembered. Those few mills that remain today should be retained, to teach future generations of a simpler era which has now long since passed.

BIBLIOGRAPHY

The following bibliography contains a list of all of the sources referred to in the preparation of this text. The author recognises his own failings in that this book does not use full citations. I have attempted to ensure that the more important points are all referenced within the text itself and hope that this mitigates the lack of more thorough citation.

The in-text references generally state both the author and the title of the work consulted. Within an individual section, multiple mentions of the same author imply further references to the piece of work originally acknowledged. Throughout this book the titles of books and periodicals are given in italics, whilst paper and article titles are given in single quotation marks. The bibliography is alphabetical, with material listed in a number of categories.

Books, Papers and Articles

1. Allison, J., *Sidelights on Tranmere*, Countyvise Ltd., 1976
2. Alsbury, Allan, *Fir Bob Land: A Look Round Higher Bebington*, Countyvise Ltd., 1999
3. Alsbury, Allan, This is Fir-Bob Land, *Port Sunlight Magazine*, Summer 1969
4. Anderson, Anne, *The Story of Bromborough*, Published Privately, 1964
5. Anon., 'Away from the Daily Grind', *Cheshire Life*, January 2006
6. Ashmore, Owen, *The Industrial Archaeology of North West England*, Manchester University Press, 1982
7. Barraclough, Geoffrey (edited), *Facsimiles of Early Cheshire Charters*, Basil Blackmore, 1957
8. Beazley, Frank C., 'Irby Windmill', *Transactions of the Historic Society of Lancashire and Cheshire*, Vol. 61 (1909)
9. Beazley, Frank C., 'Notes on Shotwick', *Transactions of the Historic Society of Lancashire and Cheshire*, Vol. 66 (1914)
10. Beazley, Frank C., *Notes on the Parish of Burton in Wirral*, Henry Young and Sons, 1908
11. Beazley, Frank C., *Thurstaston in Cheshire: An Account of the Parish, Manor and Church*, Edward Howell Ltd., 1924
12. Beazley, Frank C., 'Wirral Records of the 17th Century', *Transactions of the Historic Society of Lancashire and Cheshire*, Vol. 77 (1925)
13. Bennett, R. and Elton, J., *History of Corn Milling - Volume 1: Handstones, Slave and Cattle Mills*, Simpkin, Marshall and Company Ltd., 1898
14. Bennett R. and Elton J., *History of Corn Milling - Volume 2: Watermills and Windmills*, Simpkin, Marshall and Company Ltd., 1899 and EP Publishing Ltd., 1973
15. Bennett R. and Elton J., *History of Corn Milling - Volume 3: Feudal Laws and Customs*, Simpkin, Marshall and Company Ltd., 1900
16. Booth, P. H. W., 'Calendar of the Cheshire Trailbaston Proceedings 1353', *Cheshire History*, Vol. 11 (1983) and Vol. 12 (1983)
17. Booth, P. H. W., 'The Palatinate of Chester Inquisitions Post Mortem', *Cheshire History*, Vol. 29 (1992)
18. Booth, Paul, 'The Last Week of the Life of Edward the Black Prince', in *Contact and Exchange in Later Medieval Europe: Essays in Honour of Malcolm Vale*, Boydell & Brewer, 2012
19. Bott, Oliver, J. P., 'Cornmill Sites in Cheshire, 1066-1850' Parts 1-6, *Cheshire History*, Vol. 10 (1982), Vol. 11 (1986), Vol. 13 (1984), Vol. 14 (1984), Vol. 15 (1985), Vol. 16 (1985) and Vol. 17 (1986)
20. Boumphrey, Ian, *Yesterday's Birkenhead, A Pictorial History 1860-1960*, Published by Author, 2007
21. Boumphrey, Ian, *Yesterday's East Wirral*,

A Pictorial History 1860-1960, Published by Author, 2011

22. Boumphrey, Ian, *Yesterday's West Wirral Part One, A Pictorial History 1860-1960*, Published by Author, 2009

23. Boumphrey, Ian, *Yesterday's West Wirral Part Two, A Pictorial History 1860-1960*, Published by Author, 2010

24. Boumphrey, Ian, *Yesterday's Wallasey & New Brighton, A Pictorial History 1860-1960*, Published by Author, 2008

25. Boumphrey, Ian & Marilyn, *Yesterday's Wirral No. 6*, Published by Author, 2003

26. Boumphrey, Ian & Marilyn, *Yesterday's Wirral Pictorial History 1890 to 1953*, Published by Author, 2000

27. Brack, Alan, *The Wirral*, B. T. Batsford Ltd., 1980

28. Brown, Charles D., 'The Ancient Parish of West Kirby', *Transactions of the Historic Society of Lancashire and Cheshire*, Vol. 37 (1885)

29. Brownbill, J., 'A History of the Old Parish of Bidston, Cheshire', *Transactions of the Historic Society of Lancashire and Cheshire*, Vol. 88 (1936)

30. Brownbill, John, *West Kirby and Hilbre: A Parochial History*, Henry Young and Sons, 1928

31. Bryan, E. C., revised by Morris, D., *Willaston's Heritage*, Willaston Residents' and Countryside Society, 1997

32. Burnley, Kenneth, *Portrait of Wirral*, Hale, 1981

33. Burnley, Kenneth (edited), 'A Landmark with a History - The Story of the Mariners' Beacon', *The Wirral Journal*, Vol. 3, No. 5 (Spring 1987)

34. Burnley, Kenneth (edited), 'The First Edition Ordnance Survey of Wirral', *The Wirral Journal*, Vol. 1, No. 1 (Spring 1982)

35. Burnley, Kenneth (edited), 'The Windmills of Wirral: The Irby Mill', *The Wirral Journal*, Vol. 1, No. 3 (Autumn 1982)

36. Burnley, Kenneth (edited), 'The Windmills of Wirral: The Wallasey Mills', *The Wirral Journal*, Vol. 1, No. 2 (Summer 1982)

37. Burnley, Kenneth (edited), 'The Windmills of Wirral: The Willaston Mill', *The Wirral Journal*, Vol. 1, No. 5 (Spring 1983)

38. Burton and Neston History Society, Chambers, Susan (edited), *Neston: Stone Age to Steam Age*, Burton and Neston History Society, 2014

39. Burton and South Wirral Local History Society, Booth, P. H. W. (edited), *Burton in Wirral: A History*, Burton and South Wirral Local History Society, 1984

40. Burton and South Wirral Local History Society, Place, Geoffrey (edited), *Neston 1840-1940*, Burton and South Wirral Local History Society, 1996

41. Chitty, Gill, 'Irby Mill Excavations 1979', *Journal of Merseyside Archaeological Society*, Volume 2, 1979

42. Connah, Graham, *A Photographic Survey of Bromborough Water Mill and of its Demolition in 1949*, (Copy held at Bebington Central Library)

43. Connah, Graham, 'Bromborough Water Mill', 21st annual report of the Bromborough Society, 1953-1954

44. Coppack, Roy, 'Trafford Mill', *Cheshire History*, Vol. 31 (Spring 1993)

45. Cox, Edward W., 'The Antiquities of Storeton', *Transactions of the Historic Society of Lancashire and Cheshire*, Vol. 49 (1898)

46. Cox, John Charles, *The Royal Forests of England*, Methuen & Co., 1905

47. Craggs, Susan, 'Looking for the Tidal Mills on Bidston Moss', *Wirral Reflections*, Issue 15

48. Darby, H. C. and Maxwell, I. S, *The Domesday Geography of Northern England*, Cambridge University Press, 1962

49. Dawson, Greg, *Tingvelle: A Story of Thingwall and other North Wirral Farming Villages*, Dawson Publishing, 1993

50. Dawson, Greg, *Arwe: The Story of Arrowe, Pensby and the Liverpool Slave Trade*, Dawson Publishing, 1994

51. Dawson, Greg, *Wyrale: Wirral Topics*, Dawson Publishing, 1996

52. Dodgson, J. McNeal, *The Place-Names of Cheshire. Part I: County Name, Regional- & Forest-Names, River-Names, Road-Names, The Place-Names of Macclesfield Hundred*, English Place-Name Society No. 44, Cambridge University Press, 1970

53. Dodgson, J. McNeal, *The Place-Names of Cheshire. Part IV: The Place-Names of Broxton Hundred and Wirral Hundred*, English Place-Name Society No. 47, Cambridge University Press 1972

54. Dugdale, Sir William; Caley, John; Ellis, Henry and Bandinel, Rev. Bulkeley, *Monasticon Anglicanum:*

A History of the Abbies and other Monasteries, Hospitals, Friaries and Cathedral and Collegiate Churches and their dependencies in England and Wales, Vol. 5, London, 1825

55.   Eastwood, John, 'The Windmills of Wirral', *Cheshire Life,* May 1952

56.   Eastwood, John, *Wirral Born and Bred,* Winterbourne Press, 1993

57.   Ellison, Norman, *The Wirral Peninsula,* Redwood Burn Ltd., 1955

58.   Ellison, Norman, 'The dusty millers of Wirral', *Cheshire Life,* December 1975

59.   Fishwick, Henry (edited), *Lancashire & Cheshire Church Surveys 1649-1655,* The Record Society of Lancashire and Cheshire, Volume I, 1879

60.   Gamlin, Hilda, *Twixt Mersey and Dee,* D. Marples, 1897

61.   Harding, Stephen, *Viking Mersey: Scandinavian Wirral, West Lancashire and Chester,* Countyvise Ltd., 2002

62.   Harris, B. E. (edited), *The Victoria County History of the County of Chester,* Oxford University Press, Volume II (1979) and Volume III (1980)

63.   Hance, Edward M., 'Notes on the ancient Cheshire families of Bennett of Saughall Massey and Bennett of Barnston, with their collateral branches', *Transactions of the Historic Society of Lancashire and Cheshire,* Vol. 38 (1886)

64.   Hill, Phyllis, Heery J. and The Ranulf Higden Society (edited), *Cheshire Forest Eyre Roll 1357 - Part One: The Forest of Wirral,* The Record Society of Lancashire and Cheshire, Volume 151, 2015

65.   Irvine, W. Fergusson (edited), *An Index of Wills and Inventories now preserved in The Probate Registry at Chester from A.D. 1781 to 1790,* The Record Society of Lancashire and Cheshire, Volume XLIV, 1902

66.   Irvine, W. Fergusson, J. H. E. Bennett and others (edited), *The Cheshire Sheaf: Being Local Gleanings, Historical and Antiquarian, Relating to Cheshire, Chester and North Wales, From Many Scattered Fields,* as reprinted from the *Chester Courant* and *Cheshire Observer* and bound yearly, numerous volumes from four series referenced in text, 1878-1978

67.   Irvine, W. Fergusson, 'Notes on the Old Halls of Wirral', *Transactions of the Historic Society of Lancashire and Cheshire,* Vol. 53 (1901)

68.   Kealey, E. J., *Harvesting the Air: Windmill Pioneers in Twelfth-century England,* University of California Press, 1987

69.   Kitchingman, Joseph, 'Notes on Mother Redcap's' (partially reprinted in *The Rise and Progress of Wallasey,* 1929)

70.   Langdon, John and Watts, Martin, 'Tower Windmills in Medieval England: A Case of Arrested Development?', *Technology and Culture,* Vol. 46, No. 4 (October 2005)

71.   Lucas, A., *Wind, Water, Work: Ancient and Medieval Milling Technology,* Brill, 2005

72.   Marriott, F. E., 'Wirral Watermill Memories', *Cheshire Life,* October 1952

73.   Mesham, Arthur, 'Old Bone Wheel-Block', *Notes and Queries,* August 5th 1899

74.   Mitford Abraham, E., 'The Old Flour Mills of Wirral', *Transactions of the Historic Society of Lancashire and Cheshire,* Vol. 55 (1903-1904)

75.   Morrell, Rev. P. F. A., 'The Parish Registers of the Parish of Burton', *Journal of the Chester and North Wales Archaeological and Historic Society,* New Series Vol. 15, G. R. Griffith, 1909

76.   Morris, H., 'Willaston Tower Mill: 1: The Working Mill', *North West Mills Group Newsletter,* 1987.

77.   Mortimer, William Williams, *The History of the Hundred of Wirral; With a Sketch of the City and County of Chester,* Whittaker & Co., 1847

78.   Neilson, Harry B., *Auld Lang Syne,* Wilmer Bros., 1935

79.   Norris, J. H., 'The Water-Powered Corn Mills of Cheshire', *Transactions of the Lancashire and Cheshire Antiquarian Society,* Vol. 75 (1969)

80.   O'Brien, Pat, *Around Bebington,* Nonsuch Publishing Ltd., 1995

81.   O'Brien, Pat, *Burton to Heswall,* NPI Media Group, 1996

82.   O'Brien, Pat, *Looking Back at Ellesmere Port,* Willow Publishing, 1986

83.   O'Brien, P. A., *Our Local Heritage,* City Press of Chester Ltd., 1970

84.   Ormerod G., *The History of the County Palatine and City of Chester,* London, 1819

85.   Paterson, Don, 'The Development of Post Mills in the NW', *North West Mills Group Newsletter,* 1990

86.   Pearson, Jeffrey, *Wirral: An Illustrated*

Review, The Bluecoat Press, 2000

87. Public Record Office, *A Descriptive Catalogue of Ancient Deeds in the Public Record Office*, Volume VI, The Hereford Times Ltd., 1915

88. Public Record Office, *Calendar of Inquisitions Post Mortem and Other Analogous Documents Preserved in the Public Record Office*, Vol. II Edward I, Mackie and Co. Ltd., 1906

89. Public Record Office, *Calendar of Inquisitions Post Mortem and Other Analogous Documents Preserved in the Public Record Office*, Vol. IV Edward I, Mackie and Co. Ltd., 1913

90. Randall, David, *The Search for Old Wirral*, Countyvise Ltd., 3rd Ed., 2003

91. Rebecca, J. S., *The Old Mansions of Wallasey*, Published by Author, 1994

92. Record Commission, *Valor Ecclesiasticus*, Vol. IV, London, 1821

93. Reynolds, John, *Windmills & Watermills: Excursions in Architecture*, Hugh Evelyn, 1970

94. Rideout, Eric H., 'The Sites of Ancient Villages in Wirral', *Transactions of the Historic Society of Lancashire and Cheshire*, Vol. 77 (1925)

95. Rideout, Eric H., 'Wirral Field Names', *Transactions of the Historic Society of Lancashire and Cheshire*, Vol. 76 (1924)

96. Rideout, Eric H., 'Wirral Watersheds and River Systems and their influence on Local History', *Transactions of the Historic Society of Lancashire and Cheshire*, Vol. 74 (1922)

97. Roberts, J., 'Visit to Gayton Mill, Wirral', *North West Mills Group Newsletter*, August 1982

98. Roberts, Stephen J., *A History of Wirral*, Phillimore & Co. Ltd., 2002

99. Sanders, F. And Irvine, W. F. (edited), *Wirral Notes and Queries: Being Historical and Antiquarian Gleanings, Relating to the Hundred of Wirral*, Vols. 1 and 2 as reprinted from the *Birkenhead Advertiser*, Wilmer Bros and Co. Ltd., 1893

100. Smith, Noël E., *Almost an Island: The Story of Wallasey*, Published by Author, 1990

101. Smith, Noël E., *Sandstone and Mortar: More of old Wallasey*, Published by Author, 1992

102. Smith, P. T., 'The English Medieval Windmill', *History Today*, Vol. 28, No.4 (April 1978)

103. Stanley, Ena, *Memories of Old Eastham*, undated

104. Stewart-Brown, Ronald (edited), *Accounts of The Chamberlains and other Officers of The County of Chester 1301-1360*, The Record Society of Lancashire and Cheshire, Volume LIX, 1910

105. Stewart-Brown, R., *Birkenhead Priory and the Mersey Ferry*, The State Assurance Co., 1925

106. Stewart-Brown, R., *Cheshire Inquisitions Post Mortem: Stuart Period 1603-1660*, The Record Society of Lancashire and Cheshire, Volume LXXXIV (1934), Volume LXXXVI (1935) and Volume XCI (1938)

107. Stewart-Brown, R., 'The Disafforestation of Wirral', *Transactions of the Historic Society of Lancashire and Cheshire*, Vol. 59 (1907)

108. Stewart-Brown, R., 'The Royal Manor and Park of Shotwick', *Transactions of the Historic Society of Lancashire and Cheshire*, Vol. 64 (1912)

109. Sulley, Philip, *The Hundred of Wirral*, B. Haram and Co. Printers, 1889

110. Tait, James (edited), *The Chartulary or Register of The Abbey of St. Werburgh, Chester*, Part. 1, Chetham Society, New Series Vol. 79, 1920

111. Tait, James (edited), *The Chartulary or Register of The Abbey of St. Werburgh, Chester*, Part. 2, Chetham Society, New Series Vol. 82, 1923

112. Tait, James, *The Domesday Survey of Cheshire*, Chetham Society, New Series Vol. 75, 1916

113. The Bromborough Society, *Bromborough in Times Past*, Millennium Edition, the Bromborough Society, 2000

114. The Heswall Society, *A Wirral Album: The Photographs of E. Mitford Abraham*, The Bluecoat Press, 2003

115. The Rock Ferry Local History & Research Group, *The Changing Face of Tranmere*, Ian Boumphrey, 2011

116. The Wirral Society, *Wirral Matters*: Autumn 2008

117. Vince, John, *Discovering Windmills*, Shire Publications Ltd., 1987

118. Wailes, Rex, *A Source Book of Windmills and Watermills*, Littlehampton Book Services Ltd., 1979

119. Wailes, Rex, *The English Windmill*, Routledge & Kegan Paul Ltd., 2nd imp., 1967

120. Watts, Martin, *Water and Wind Power*, Shire Publications Ltd., 2005

121. Wetscott, Thomas, *Landmarks of Old Wallasey Village 1859*, St. Hilary's Church, 2004

122. Williams, H. and Crompton, J., 'The Windmills of Wirral', *Journals of the North-Western*

Society for Industrial Archaeology and History, 1976 and 1977 (addenda)

123. Woods, E. C. and Brown P. C., *The Rise and Progress of Wallasey*, 2nd Ed., The Scholar Press Limited, 1974

124. Woods, E. C., 'Further Notes on the Penkett Family', *Transactions of the Historic Society of Lancashire and Cheshire*, Vol. 78 (1926)

125. Woods, E. C., 'Smuggling in Wirral', *Transactions of the Historic Society of Lancashire and Cheshire*, Vol. 79 (1927)

126. Woods, E. C., 'The Journal of John Hough-Lord of the Manor of Liscard', *Transactions of the Historic Society of Lancashire and Cheshire*, Vol. 72 (1920)

127. Yorke, Stan, *The Industrial Revolution Explained*, Countryside Books, 2005

128. Yorke, Stan, *Windmills and Waterwheels Explained*, Countryside Books, 2006

Maps and Sea Charts

129. *A Survey And Mapp of Edward Green Esquire's Land in the Township Poolton Lancelin*, 1721, (Green estate map)

130. Bainbridge, Thomas (surveyor), *A Survey and Valuation of the Estates belonging to the Right Honourable Charles, Earl of Shrewsbury*, 1788-1789, C.R.O. MF 387 (Shrewsbury estate maps of Brimstage, Barnston, Little Neston and Oxton)

131. Bennison, *Map of Liverpool and Environs*, 1835

132. Bryant, Andrew, *Map of the County Palatine of Chester from an Actual Survey by A. Bryant in the years 1829, 1830 & 1831*, 1831

133. Burdett, Peter, *A Chart of the Harbour of Liverpool*, 1771

134. Burdett, Peter P., *A Survey of the County Palatine of Chester*, 1777

135. Burdett, Peter P., *A Survey of the County Palatine of Chester, Reprinted in Facsimile with an Introduction by J. B. Harley and P. Laxton*, Lund Humphries, 1974

136. Cheshire tithe maps and apportionments for all Wirral townships, Cheshire Record Office

137. Collins, Capt. Greenville, *A New & Exact Survey of the River Dee or Chester-Water*, 1689

138. Eyes, Charles (surveyor), *Township of Hooton surveyed by Charles Eyes for Sir Wm Stanley*, 1776, C.R.O. D 293/7 (Stanley estate map)

139. Fearon S. and Eyes J., *A Description and Chart of the Sea Coast from Chester Bar to Formby Point*, 1738

140. Greenwood, Christopher, *Map of the County Palatine of Chester from an Actual Survey made in the year 1819*, 1819 (also a revised edition published 1830)

141. Hunter, *A New Map of the Hundred of Wirral, with the Line of Canal from the Chester Canal Bason to the River Mersey*, 1810

142. Lawton, *Map of Birkenhead Estate of F. R. Price Esquire*, 1824

143. Mackay-Math, John, *An Abridged Plan of the River Dee and Hyle Lake*, 1732

144. *Map of the Manor of Hooton and Lands in the Townships of Childer Thornton and Little Sutton... belonging to Sir Tho. Stanley Massey Stanley Bart.*, 1825, C.R.O. D 293/8 (Stanley estate map)

145. Morden, Robert, *The County Palatinate of Chester*, 1695

146. *Reprint of the first edition of the one-inch Ordnance Survey of England and Wales – Denbigh & Wirral*, David & Charles, 2nd Ed., 1979.

147. *Reprint of the first edition of the one-inch Ordnance Survey of England and Wales – Northwich & Warrington*, David & Charles, 2nd Ed., 1979.

148. Smith, *A Map of Wirral and Chester*, 1808

149. Speed, John, Map of Cheshire within - *The Theatre of the Empire of Great Britaine*, 1610

150. Taylor, Thomas (surveyor), *A Survey of the Mannor of Bidstone in Cheshire in England belonging to the Right Honourable John, Lord Kingston*, 1665, C.R.O. D 4938 (Kingston survey)

151. Williamson, Robert, *Liverpool and Parkgate Harbours*, 1766 (included in *The Rise and Progress of Wallasey*)

152. Ordnance Survey maps of Cheshire, c.1875 and c.1910

Directories, Newspapers, Unpublished Documents, Wills and other Record Office Material

153. Account Book of Sir Rowland Stanley Bart, 1746-1751, T.N.A. D 4962/1, (Copy at Bebington Central Library)

154. Agreement dated 1600 (Miscellaneous Deeds, Stoke and Stanney Estate), C.R.O. EEC 33588/12

155. Alsbury, Allan, *Bromborough Mill: Drawings, Photographs & Notes*, 1983, (Copies held at Bebington Central Library and Cheshire Record Office)

156. *Bagshaw's Cheshire Directory*, George Ridge, 1850

157. Connah, Graham, The Diary of G. E. Connah Volume 2, consulted entries between 1948 and 1950, (Copy held at Bebington Central Library)

158. Cowdroy, W., *The Directory and Guide for the City and County of Chester*, W. Cowdroy, 1789

159. Death Registration of Samuel Lightbound of Tranmere, 1863, Mills Archive, Don Paterson Collection, DONP-14642

160. 'Gibbet Mill Falling into Decay', *Liverpool Daily Post*, 27th September 1962

161. 'Higher Bebington Mill', *Liverpool Daily Post*, 9th March 1966

162. 'Historic Mill at Bebington', *Liverpool Daily Post*, 30th September 1933

163. Inquisition Post Mortem of Sir Hugh Cholmondeley Kt., 1597, C.R.O. DCH/C/479

164. *Kelly's Directory of Cheshire*, Kelly's Directories Ltd.,1902, 1906 and 1910

165. Lease of Bromborough Watermill, 1777, (Typed copy of lease previously in possession of E. Ellis, courtesy of Susan Nicholson)

166. 'Luxury Transformation for Historic Windmill', *Liverpool Daily Post*, 16th August 1991

167. McMillan, N. F., Journal of Mrs. N. F. McMillan, Notes on Bromborough Windmill drive (1970) and Notes on Raby Mere leat (1956) (Copies courtesy of Susan Nicholson)

168. *Morris and Co.'s Commercial Directory and Gazetteer of Cheshire*, Morris & Co., 1864

169. 'New Lease of Life for Wirral Mills', *Liverpool Daily Post*, 31st March 1962

170. *Post Office Directory of Cheshire*, Kelly & Co., 1857 and 1878

171. *Slater's Directory of Cheshire and Liverpool*, Isaac Slater, 1883

172. *Slater's Royal National Commercial Directory of Cheshire*, Isaac Slater, 1869 and 1902

173. *The Bebington News*, 1st December 1979

174. *White's Cheshire Directory*, Francis White & Co., 1860

175. Will and Inventory of James Carter of Eastham, 1602 and 1608, (Cheshire Record Office, transcribed inventory courtesy of Susan Nicholson)

176. Will and Inventory of Thomas Sparke of Eastham, 1591, (Cheshire Record Office)

177. Will of John Bibby of Liscard, 1782, (Cheshire Record Office)

178. Will of John Davies of Little Neston, 1741, (Cheshire Record Office)

179. Will of William Lightbound of Bromborough, 1767, (Courtesy of Simon Lightbound)

180. Will of William Lightbound of Willaston Mill, 1797, (Courtesy of Simon Lightbound)

181. 'Willaston Windmill', *Cheshire Observer*, 2nd April 1938

182. *William's Commercial Directory of Chester*, J. Williams, 1846

183. 'Windmill at Willaston', *Liverpool Daily Post*, 31st March 1938

184. 'Wirral Landmark May Have to be Demolished', *Liverpool Echo*, 10th June 1955

This book has two indices. The first of these is the General Index, which covers people, places and subjects. Secondly is the Index of Mills; this lists all of the mills described on Wirral, and might be usefully employed in conjunction with Appendix B. Given the entries relating to specific mills on Wirral are numerous and form this book's principal theme, it seemed most convenient to keep them separate from the General Index. Illustrations are not indexed, since they are described by the List of Illustrations at the start of the book.

General Index

Index of Mills

About the Author

Rowan Patel was born in Liverpool in 1991 and grew up in Bromborough on Wirral. He developed keen interests in both local history and industrial archaeology at an early age, for he felt naturally inclined to investigate the history of his Wirral home. His enthusiasm for historical research has led to the publication of industrial history articles in local and national periodicals. These have all been well received. Traditional milling is a topic which has intrigued him for many years. Whilst at school it became apparent to him that much research remained to be carried out on Wirral's mills, a deficiency which he decided needed resolving. He began studying for a Master's degree in Chemistry at the University of York in 2010 and graduated in 2014. He now works for a glass and ceramics manufacturing company in Stoke-on-Trent, a city containing much of historical interest.